CW00428461

RAPT
THE

BY

SANDRA MARTON

MILLS & BOON LIMITED
ETON HOUSE 18–24 PARADISE ROAD
RICHMOND SURREY TW9 1SR

First published in Great Britain 1985
by Mills & Boon Limited

© Sandra Myles 1985

Australian copyright 1985
Philippine copyright 1992
This edition 1992

ISBN 0 263 77735 9

Set in Plantin 10 on 11 pt.
01-9209-53900

Typeset in Great Britain by County Typesetters, Kent

Made and printed in Great Britain

CHAPTER ONE

THE SUN was rising over the Mediterranean. Like a great
orange ball of light, it seemed to balance precariously on
the sapphire-blue water before it rose into the paler sky,
touching the clouds with flame. Amanda Sutton shifted
wearily in her seat in the jumbo jet and pressed closer to
the 747's tiny window. Her head ached after so many
hours of flying, but, at least for the moment, the
spectacular view out of her window was enough to make
her ignore her aching head and complete feeling of
exhaustion. She sighed and pressed her cool fingertips to
her temples, trying to ease the throbbing pain that
seemed to match the monotonous hum of the plane's
engines, then smoothed back the few strands of silky
golden hair that had escaped from her usual neat
chignon. Finally she leaned back in the hard seat and
closed her eyes.

'Don't fall asleep now, for heaven's sake, Amanda!
We'll be landing in Morocco in half an hour or so.' The
plump, plain-faced woman in the next seat rubbed her
eyes and yawned loudly. 'Although I wouldn't mind a
little nap myself. Boy, these seats aren't exactly made for
comfort, are they?'

Amanda smiled sympathetically at her companion.
'No, they're not, Helen. I've never felt so tired in my life,
and I feel as if my clothing is wrinkled from head to toe.'

Helen Rogers looked enviously at the girl next to her.
Amanda's blonde hair gleamed, reflecting the rays of the
rising sun. Her large, long-lashed blue eyes were clear
and serene above her small, straight nose and delicate,

5

yet ripe mouth. She wore a conservative, classically cut navy suit, but even the austere severity of its neat lines couldn't fully disguise the lush contours beneath it. The suit was smooth and unwrinkled and looked as crisp and as fresh as it had hours before.

'I don't think you have much to worry about, Amanda,' Helen said wryly. She glanced down at her own wrinkled dress and grimaced in distaste. 'I mean, I know it's fantastic to be able to fly from New York to this. . .this Arabian Nights fairyland in just eight hours, but how come you look perfect, as always, and I look like a mess?' A pleasant grin lit her homely face. 'Maybe that's one reason I'm a secretary and you're the boss.'

Amanda smiled tiredly and shook her head. 'Thanks for the kind words,' she said. 'I'm so nervous and jittery that every little bit of confidence helps. I just can't stop worrying about this assignment.'

'What's there to worry about? You must know your stuff or the big boys upstairs wouldn't have tapped you to be Mr Pauling's assistant on this job. And nobody knows better than I do how hard you've prepared for this, going over plans and reports these past few weeks.'

Amanda sighed softly and leaned back in her seat. 'Well, I admit I've done a little work getting ready, but. . .'

'Come on, Amanda, you can't fool me—I'm your secretary, remember? I know how many nights you stayed late at the office, going over everything you could get your hands on about Morocco and this Sheikh what's-his-name.'

'Nicholas ben Saad, you mean. That's exactly what I'm worried about—after all, he's going to be the most important client I've ever had, and the more I know about the man, the more nervous I get. He's supposed to be a tough, shrewd businessman, Helen. Every project he's been involved in brings in millions.'

'And that's bad?' Helen asked in mock amusement.

'No, of course not. It's just that he has a reputation for being arrogant and self-centred. And I keep wondering how he's going to take to dealing with a woman—after all, things are different in this part of the world.'

Helen snorted derisively and laughed. 'Amanda, you know Morocco is a modern country. I see the ads from their tourist bureau on TV all the time. You know, Tangier, Marrakesh. . .the whole bit. Besides, would the company be sending women there otherwise? As for how the Sheikh will react to you. . .' She paused and rummaged under her seat. 'Here,' she said, tossing a copy of *WE* magazine into Amanda's lap, 'take a look at that. According to the gossip columnists, your boy has other interests besides making money. If what they say is true, you ought to score points on looks alone! Well, you asked me,' she added quickly, bristling at the look of annoyance that passed over Amanda's face. Helen struggled to her feet and smoothed down her skirt. 'I'm going to head for the powder-room. Maybe a splash of cold water on my face will help me feel better.'

Amanda settled back in her seat and tried to ignore the tight knot of apprehension within her. She glanced down at the magazine in her lap. There was no time in her well-organised life for such frivolous reading material, and she opened the glossy cover with curiosity, flipping through the flashy pages until she came to one that was dog-eared. Under the heading WE SEE was a colour photograph of Nicholas ben Saad. The photographer had apparently caught him just as he was about to drive off in a shiny red Ferrari. There were sunglasses perched on his dark, slightly curling hair and he was wearing a close-fitting knitted shirt. His handsome, scowling face and upper torso were turned towards the camera, and even the flat,

two-dimensional photograph couldn't completely hide
the lean yet muscular power in his arms and shoulders.
Shockingly blue eyes, no doubt a heritage from his
French mother, seemed to reflect anger at this violation
of his privacy, and there was an arrogant, sensual cruelty
in the set of his mouth. He had about him the look of a
beautiful yet deadly jungle cat and, involuntarily,
Amanda shuddered. She scanned the brief, breathy text
that accompanied the picture. It gushed:

> Baron of the Boudoir and Boardroom, Sheikh Nicholas
> ben Saad, wealthy racing enthusiast and industrialist,
> caught by our camera at Le Mans. WE wonder: was
> Nicky there to win another trophy on the track or to
> break the hearts of another bevy of beauties? Either
> way, WE know: Nicky is a winner!

Amanda glanced back at the photograph. You may be a
winner, she thought grimly, but so am I.

She'd had to be, she mused, closing her eyes wearily.
She'd come a long way from Santa Margarita, California,
and her wide-eyed pleasure at winning a full scholarship
to UCLA. Her modest goal had been to become a maths
teacher, something her high school guidance counsellor
had assured her was the proper career for a young woman
with a talent for numbers, but a romantic, impetuous
elopement in her freshman year had altered her life for
ever. The marriage was doomed from the start; the
divorce only months later left her penniless and alone.
Her scholarship was gone, lost when she had dropped out
of university to support her student husband; there was
no alimony to fall back on because she'd refused to ask
for any from the man who had given her nothing but
heartache; and even to think of returning home, defeated
and wounded, to live with her mother's bitter fury at the

mess she had made of her life, was out of the question. She had gone to work as a waitress, waiting on tables half the night so she could go to college by day, moving in a kind of dream world of isolation and self-pity, until one morning, seeking shelter from a sudden rainstorm, she had stumbled into an auditorium and listened to a campus recruiter from Olsen & Tibbs talk about engineering and the limitless opportunities open to talented, determined women in this almost exclusively male field.

From that moment on Amanda had known what she wanted. Power, money, success were all there, if she had enough dedication to go after them. Six months short of graduation, she signed on as a trainee with the giant corporation, rushing to classes at night and working harder than anyone else in the office by day. When, after a year, her efforts were rewarded with a transfer to the more prestigious New York office, no one had been surprised, least of all Amanda. Now her promotion had come through and with it this assignment, a plum sought after by all the men with whom she worked. If she succeeded, she was on her way to the top. If she failed. . .she swallowed hard and refused to consider it.

Something brushed against her side and her eyes flew open. Helen Rogers was fastening her seatbelt and she smiled apologetically.

'Sorry, A.S., I didn't mean to startle you, but it doesn't pay to doze off now anyway. The seatbelt sign just came on, and I think we're going to be landing in a couple of minutes.' She bent her dark head towards Amanda and lowered her voice to an exaggerated whisper. 'I passed Tim Pauling on the way to the bathroom. Doesn't that man ever smile?'

'Not at me, he doesn't.' Amanda shrugged her shoulders and a tiny frown creased the smooth skin around her mouth. 'Let's face it, Helen—he's not exactly delighted that I'm to be his assistant on this job, and he hasn't kept it a secret, either.'

'But it's not because you aren't capable, A.S. Look, some guys just refuse to admit that a woman can do a man's job, and Pauling happens to be one of them. Don't let him get you down. Remember, all the girls in the office are betting on you!'

There was an unexpected lurch and gentle bump, and Amanda realised with surprise that the plane had landed. She took a deep breath.

'Well, here we go,' she said, getting to her feet. As she did, a hand gripped her elbow.

'You seemed so deep in conversation that I wasn't sure you knew we'd landed. I didn't think girl talk could be so interesting.' It was Tim Pauling, her boss. His round face was swollen and puffy from lack of sleep and his balding head glimmered with perspiration.

'Helen and I were talking about the Sheikh,' Amanda answered pleasantly, choosing to ignore the sarcastic challenge of his words. 'I've been thinking about the presentation we're going to make tomorrow.'

Pauling stepped aside as Amanda started up the aisle ahead of him. 'Well, that makes two of us, kid. I certainly hope it goes well. I only met the man that one time he was in New York last year while you were on vacation, but he impressed me as the type who's hard to please. You may have a rough time convincing him that we've got to use some lightweight materials if we're going to build that irrigation plant at the price he wants.'

'I have all the facts and figures right here, Tim,' Amanda answered, patting the briefcase she held cradled in her arms. 'Don't worry, I'm sure I can handle it.'

'I'm sure you can, Sutton. Why should I doubt it? After all, the powers that be handpicked you for this job,

and who am I to question the wisdom of their decision?'
He spoke in a light, bantering tone, with a smile on his
face, but Amanda stiffened at the hint of anger that lay
just under his words.

'I can handle it,' she repeated tersely as they hurried
down the ramp from the plane and stepped aside, waiting
for Helen to join them. 'I've done my homework.'

Tim Pauling muttered a response, but it was drowned
out by Helen, who stood gaping at the terminal building
they had entered.

'Boy, oh, boy!' she breathed in open admiration.
'What a gorgeous place this is!'

Tim scanned its soaring modern lines and smiled. 'It is
quite something,' he said. 'Look at all that glass and
steel—must have cost a small fortune to build!' He
chuckled raspily. 'Too bad Olsen & Tibbs didn't get a
chance to bid on this one, isn't it?'

Amanda nodded in silent agreement. The building was
indeed impressive in its stark, contemporary beauty. For
the first time since boarding the plane in New York, she
felt caught up in a wave of excitement as the sudden
reality of their arrival in this exotic place swept over her.
It was rather early and the building wasn't very crowded,
but there were still enough people hurrying about to
provide an intriguing panorama of sights and sounds.
There were men in Western clothing as well as some in
flowing Arab caftans, but most fascinating of all were the
women. They seemed to be wearing everything from the
latest designer jeans to expensive suits and dresses, and
there was even a handful in graceful, traditional robes
and head-coverings. Trying to see everything, yet hurrying to keep up with Tim's brisk pace, Amanda suddenly
tripped over something underfoot. She bumped sharply
into an old man and her briefcase and handbag went
flying.

'I'm terribly sorry!' she gasped, scurrying to retrieve her things. The old man, unmoving, scowled darkly at her.

'Watch where you walk,' he muttered in heavily accented English.

Amanda stared at him in surprise. 'Well, I thought I was,' she said briskly, 'but, you see, you had your suitcase stuck out here in the middle of the floor, and. . .'

'I keep suitcase wherever I like!' the old man thundered as a small group of passers-by paused and watched with interest. He stabbed a gnarled cane at Amanda and she shrank back. 'You must watch, woman. Is not for me to watch out for you.'

Amanda felt herself stiffening with anger and indignation. 'Now, just one minute,' she said heatedly. 'I've already apologised to you, even though it was actually your fault that I stumbled. You might at least be civil about it!'

The old man's eyes burned with ill-disguised contempt. 'Woman should watch where she walks,' he repeated, 'not me.'

'Is that so? Well, let me tell you something, mister——'

'That's enough,' snapped Tim Pauling, cutting her off in mid-sentence. He grabbed her roughly by the arm and hustled her off into a corner while she spluttered furiously.

'Terrific,' he snarled, 'just terrific! You're not in this place ten minutes and you've gotten yourself into a public confrontation! Where do you think you are, kid, on a New York City subway platform?'

'Now, wait a minute, Tim. I didn't do anything to cause a. . .a confrontation, as you call it. That old man was just plain rude. He seems to think that just because I'm a woman he can do whatever he pleases.'

'Damned right he can, kid. That old guy belongs here, and we don't. Suppose you try and remember that. You knew what to expect once we got here—I gave you all the background material to read weeks ago. This is a modern country, but women have a different status here, at least among some segments of the. . .'

'Of the older population,' Amanda parroted. 'I know the cultural material by heart. But if you think I'm going to turn into a second-class citizen just because of some sheikh. . .'

'Listen, young woman,' Tim Pauling whispered angrily, 'Nicholas ben Saad has nothing whatsoever to do with this. Use your head, Sutton. If he felt that way, would New York have chosen you for this job? If you think I'm going to baby-sit you all the time I'm over here, you can forget all about it. Sooner or later, I'm going back to the States and you'll be on your own. How will you manage then, just tell me that?'

Amanda pulled free of his restraining hand and looked at him steadily. 'You needn't worry about me, Tim,' she answered, her words clipped and precise. 'I'm fully aware of my responsibilities. But that doesn't mean I'm going to give up my rights.'

Tim Pauling sighed wearily and rolled his eyes up to the ceiling. 'What is the matter with you? Can't you get that chip off your shoulder? All I'm telling you is that you'll have to remember the ground rules if you don't want to mess things up for both of us.'

'And just what are the ground rules?' she challenged.

'The ground rules, of course,' a silky voice interjected, 'are that old men are sometimes irritable and discourteous, no matter what their nationality.'

Amanda and her boss turned around in surprise. An elderly, white-haired gentleman, impeccably dressed in a dark grey Savile Row suit, bowed deeply. At the snap of his fingers, a uniformed chauffeur stepped forward and took their hand luggage from them.

'Allow me to introduce myself,' the stranger said to Tim Pauling with polite formality. 'I am Abdul Gamal, executive assistant to His Excellency Sheikh Nicholas ben Saad, and I hope to prove to you both that I am one old man who proves the rules wrong. I had planned to greet you at your aircraft, but it landed a bit earlier than I had expected. I trust your journey was a pleasant one. I only regret that your secretary had such an unfortunate introduction to our country.'

Tim cleared his throat and tightened his grip on Amanda's arm. Behind them, Helen's sudden giggle turned quickly into an elaborate cough after a quick warning glare from Tim.

'Our flight was just fine, sir,' he said, extending his hand to Gamal. 'I'm Timothy Pauling. This,' he added, nodding towards Helen, 'is my secretary—mine and Miss Sutton's. Miss Sutton is my assistant.' His voice trailed off into silence, and the old man turned his piercing gaze towards Amanda.

'Of course—how clumsy of me! How do you do, Miss Rogers? And Miss Sutton—I've looked forward to meeting you. I had no idea someone with your responsibilities would be so young and, I might add, so lovely.'

Amanda smiled coolly as Abdul Gamal bowed cordially. 'Thank you for the compliment, Mr Gamal. I assume that was a compliment and not an expression of concern for my abilities.'

Tim pinched her arm fiercely, but Abdul Gamal merely smiled again.

'I'm quite sure you're capable, Miss Sutton. It's simply that you've taken me by surprise—a most pleasant one at that. But surely you all must be exhausted. It's only a short drive to town.' He motioned the chauffeur on ahead and led them towards the exit doors.

'Don't we have to stop at Customs?' Helen asked hopefully. 'I was kind of looking forward to having my passport stamped.'

Mr Gamal frowned slightly, as if he'd just tasted something unpleasant. 'You are guests of Nicholas ben Saad,' he said stiffly. 'Such procedures are unnecessary.'

The heavy glass doors whisked open automatically and the dry heat and musky smells of the North African morning enveloped them. Amanda drew in her breath sharply. She felt as if she had walked into a sauna, and she hurried into the long black limousine which awaited them at the kerb.

'Get a load of this,' Helen whispered breathily as she scrambled into the car. 'Not bad, hmm?'

The interior of the cool, air-conditioned Rolls-Royce was all cream-coloured, glove-soft leather, silky and sensual to the touch. The seats were as comfortable as those in a fine living-room, and Amanda sank back gratefully. There was a television, a telephone, and a bar from which Mr Gamal offered them chilled drinks while the chauffeur stowed their luggage in the trunk. As soon as they pulled out into the stream of steadily moving light traffic, Amanda's attention was drawn to the changing scenes visible through the tinted windows of the Rolls-Royce, and she paid scant attention to the ebb and flow of polite conversation that swirled around her. They were passing through the suburbs of Casablanca, and in many ways it looked the same as any early morning scene on the outskirts of a major city. There were people hurrying to work, of course, but some of them were on bicycles or motor scooters. And, as she had noticed at the airport, there was an easy blend of traditional and modern styles of dress to be seen along the dusty road. Gradually the

graceful silhouette of the city began to appear in the
distance, and soon they were driving within a maze of
angular skyscrapers and heavy automobile traffic. The
Rolls made a sweeping turn down a wide, tree-lined
boulevard which seemed to have a kind of European
charm about it, and after several more minutes the car
swung into a broad, semi-circular driveway.

'One of our newest hotels,' Abdul Gamal explained as
the door to the limousine opened. 'His Excellency
thought you would be comfortable here, and it is quite
near your branch office.' He smiled at Tim. 'We're very
proud of the Palm, even though it wasn't built by your
firm.'

Tim laughed politely, but Amanda was too tired to
manage more than a smile. The hotel manager seemed to
have been waiting for them, along with what appeared to
be a small army of bellhops. Bowing deeply, he escorted
them through the handsome lobby, proudly pointing out
the hotel's restaurants, lounges, and boutiques. They
entered a modern glass-enclosed lift, and as they were
whisked upwards Amanda stifled a yawn. Her eyes met
Abdul Gamal's and she smiled in apology.

'I'm sorry,' she began, but the old man shrugged and
cut her off in mid-sentence with a sweeping wave of his
hand.

'There's no need to be, Miss Sutton.' He turned to the
hotel manager. 'Mr Baran,' he said smoothly, 'I'm sure
our guests will want to ask you a thousand questions
later, but I think perhaps they would like to get to their
rooms just now. Would you be kind enough to see Mr
Pauling and Miss Rogers to their accommodation? I'll
escort Miss Sutton to hers.'

At last, to her great relief, Amanda found herself
standing outside the door to a room on the hotel's top
floor, just down the hall from Tim's. Abdul Gamal

handed her the keys with a small bow.

'I hope you enjoy your stay with us,' he said. 'And I think you'll like your room. The view from up here is quite beautiful, I'm told. I couldn't help but notice that you seemed interested in seeing everything you could as we drove here.'

'I do want to see everything,' Amanda admitted, warming to the friendly tone of his voice. 'I've never been in this part of the world before. Actually,' she added wistfully, 'I've never been anywhere, except for my home town and New York City.' She unlocked the door and turned towards the old man. 'Mr Gamal,' she said haltingly, 'I just want to assure you that I'm really looking forward to this assignment. It's important to me, and you can count on me to do my best.'

Abdul Gamal's eyebrows arched as he looked at her. 'Why would I think otherwise, Miss Sutton?'

Amanda could feel the colour rising to her cheeks as she fumbled for words. 'It's just that I get the feeling you expected someone more experienced, or at least someone older than I am. And I'm not usually as impolite as I appeared to be at the airport.'

'Nonsense, my dear. You were tired from your long journey and that old fool was rude. As for the kind of person I expected—well, I'm sure Olsen & Tibbs would not have placed you in a position of such responsibility if you were not deserving of it.' He smiled slightly, but his dark eyes remained cool and impassive. 'I must admit that I am somewhat surprised, however. We did not anticipate that someone as young and attractive as you would be a field consultant.'

Amanda drew herself up to her full five feet four inches and stared steadily at him. 'I'm twenty-six years old, Mr Gamal. I'm hardly a child. And, in case you're interested, I have a Bachelor of Science degree from a

very reputable university. Is there anything else you want
to know?'

A flicker of amusement seemed to pass over the old
man's face. 'No, I think not, Miss Sutton. I think I have
learned more than enough to satisfy the Sheikh. He often
relies upon me for first impressions.'

Amanda winced inwardly. 'And recommendations?
Does he rely upon you for those, too?'

Mr Gamal frowned. 'I'm afraid I don't understand
you, Miss Sutton.'

'I think you do, Mr Gamal. I think you're going to
recommend that I be replaced by someone older and
more experienced. I'd even bet that you'd prefer that my
replacement should be a man.'

Abdul Gamal drew himself up haughtily and stared at
her. 'I would never be so presumptuous, my dear young
woman. What is more, neither should you be.' After a
few seconds of silence, he smiled politely and took her
hand in his. 'I really think you need some rest, Miss
Sutton. They tell me that jet lag is quite common after so
long a flight.' He bowed slightly and stepped back from
the doorway. 'I look forward to seeing you at tomorrow's
meeting.'

Amanda managed to maintain a shaky smile until
finally she had closed the door behind her. Then she let
out her breath in an angry hiss and kicked off her shoes.
'Jet lag!' she muttered grimly. Well, it was either that or
insanity, she thought. In less than an hour, she'd
managed to pick a fight with a stranger, infuriate her
boss, and anger the Sheikh's representative. 'You're
really scoring on all fronts, Amanda,' she murmured
aloud as she opened one of her suitcases and began to
unpack. She padded swiftly from the suitcase to the
closet, rapidly and neatly hanging her clothing on the
polished chrome rack. What had possessed her to behave

so badly? She'd waited so long for this chance, worked so hard, and now she'd very nearly ruined it all. Maybe she did have a chip on her shoulder, as Tim said, but it was easy for a man to be smug about the problems a woman faced in business. It had been necessary for Amanda to learn to survive in a man's world, where femininity was sometimes misinterpreted as softness of purpose, and good looks were often suspect. And Tim Pauling wasn't making the situation any easier. It had been management's decision to promote her, and their decision to offer her this assignment. Tim Pauling had made no bones about his feelings.

'I've never worked with a woman before,' he'd said bluntly. 'Frankly, I don't see any place for them in engineering. It's nothing personal, you understand, it's just that I'm like an old dog. It's too late for me to learn any new tricks.'

'Then why don't you ask them to reassign me?' she had asked, choking back her anger.

Tim had shrugged eloquently. 'If it were that simple, I would. But the top brass are on this affirmative action kick, and it would look bad for me if I bucked the trend. Just do your job, follow my instructions, and we'll manage. Who knows? You might even be an asset. I hear the Sheikh has an eye for good-looking broads.'

He had laughed and slapped her on the back, but Amanda still smarted at the memory.

She hung the last of her things in the closet and sighed wearily. It was too late to undo any of her mistakes; the best she could hope for was that she would start over with a clean slate at the next day's meeting. Stifling a yawn, she glanced at her watch, and realised it was still set to New York time. It might be late morning here in Morocco, but as far as she was concerned it was not even dawn. She pulled the tortoiseshell clips from her hair and her long golden tresses fell silkily down her back. She padded barefoot to the tiny balcony and peered down into the streets below. The city was fully awake now and teeming with life. Just a few hours' rest, she thought, and then she would go out and explore the wide boulevards and the narrow, winding side-streets she had only had a tantalising glimpse of earlier.

She slipped between the cool linen sheets of the bed. Tomorrow would be a long, difficult day. Tim was already half convinced she wasn't up to this job, and if she was right about Abdul Gamal's reaction to her Sheikh Nicholas ben Saad wasn't going to be too pleased, either. 'Welcome to Morocco, Amanda,' she whispered into her pillow, then her long lashes closed over her eyes, and she slept.

CHAPTER TWO

AMANDA awoke with a start. There was a persistent ringing noise in the room, and it took her a while to realise it was the telephone. She reached for it groggily.

'Good morning, kid. Did you ever wake up long enough to go out on the town last night?'

She rubbed her eyes and tried to make some sense out of Tim's words. 'What time is it?' she asked huskily.

'It's time to rise and shine, Sutton,' he laughed. 'You slept right around the clock. I knocked on your door late last night, but I figured you never knew it. There's a cab picking us up in half an hour—better get moving!'

Amanda hung up the phone and groaned. She remembered waking once and ordering sandwiches and coffee from room service. She had eaten while leafing through a guide book and then collapsed back on the bed. It didn't seem possible she had managed to sleep so long; still, she felt rested, and at least the awful headache of the day before was gone. The air-conditioning had somehow failed during the hours she had been asleep, and she was immediately and uncomfortably aware of the heat. Pushing damp tendrils of hair off her forehead, she went to the balcony and looked out. She could almost see shimmering waves of heat rising from the white pavement below.

She showered quickly in the luxuriously appointed bathroom, but the cooling effect of the water seemed to last only seconds. Then she wrapped herself in a thick, soft towel and looked quickly through the clothes she had so carefully hung in the closet. All her neat suits and dresses, so proper for New York, seemed too heavy to be worn comfortably in this oppressive heat. Finally she grudgingly selected a pale blue silk dress. It was not really as businesslike a garment as she would have liked for this important meeting, but it was, at least, long-sleeved and full-skirted, although the thin fabric clung to her breasts and narrow waist more than she liked. She wound her long hair into its familiar chignon, added the barest touch of pale pink lipstick, and she was ready.

It was only a brief taxi ride to the Sheikh's office, through the most modern and fashionable section of the city. A private lift took Amanda and Tim to the top floor of a soaring skyscraper and, within minutes, they entered the most impressive boardroom she had ever seen. A magnificent oval conference table of dark, highly polished wood filled the centre of the room, which was panelled in rich walnut. The floor was an intricate mosaic of ceramic tiles in vibrant colours which were picked up by the Impressionist paintings hung on the long walls. There were several men standing around in small groups, chatting quietly, and Amanda scanned their faces anxiously, but none of them was Nicholas ben Saad. Suddenly a door at the room's far end opened and Abdul Gamal entered.

'Here we go,' whispered Tim, and Amanda noted with grim satisfaction that his bald head was gleaming with nervous perspiration.

Immediately, all conversation in the room ceased as everyone turned expectantly towards the open door. Abdul Gamal nodded politely and stepped aside, and Amanda's throat constricted drily as Nicholas ben Saad strode into the room. Tall, lean, broad-shouldered, he carried himself with a regal, almost arrogant assurance that belied the fact that he was scarcely past his thirty-third birthday. The photograph of him had not exaggerated his looks; in fact, he was even more handsome than she had expected. His eyes were a startling ice blue, and they swept the room with something akin to boredom until they settled on Amanda. The men clustered before him parted like the sea as the Sheikh walked directly towards her.

'Your Excellency,' Tim said nervously, 'it's a great pleasure to see you again.'

The Sheikh smiled and shook Tim's extended hand, but his piercing eyes never wavered from Amanda. She felt her cheeks beginning to colour, but she stared back at him in silence.

'I'm delighted to see you, too, Mr Pauling,' he answered. His voice was deep and pleasant, with just the slightest French accent.

'May I present my assistant, the co-ordinator on this project, Miss. . .?'

'I know who this is, Mr Pauling,' Nicholas ben Saad said softly. He took Amanda's hand in his and raised it to his lips. 'Amanda Sutton, of course,' he murmured, his eyes moving slowly across her face and then down her body. Amanda stiffened under his deliberate, penetrating gaze. Her hand, where his mouth had touched it, seemed to tingle. 'Mr Gamal was quite right, Miss Sutton,' he added, smiling at her, 'you are indeed not quite what I had expected.'

Amanda pulled her hand free of his and forced herself to look directly into his eyes. 'I trust you expected a well prepared, knowledgeable co-ordinator, Your Excellency, and, I assure you, that is precisely what I am.'

His arrogant face was softened by a sardonic smile. 'Indeed?' he replied. 'We shall see.'

Introductions were made and everyone was seated at the conference table. The Sheikh made some brief opening remarks, defining in precise terms the need for an irrigation project in the arid wastes in the eastern portion of the country, and specifying the interests of the various government officials, bankers, and industrialists present. He spoke with an intensity and intelligence that kept all eyes riveted on him. Then he turned the meeting over to Tim, who made the Olsen & Tibbs presentation, using many of the charts and facts Amanda had laboriously prepared, but never mentioning her name. Throughout Tim's speech, she was uncomfortably aware of the Sheikh's eyes upon her, but the expression in them was unfathomable. There was a short question and answer period during which Nicholas ben Saad directed several penetrating questions first at Tim and then at her, but Amanda was at ease with the material and answered him coolly and efficiently. Finally he nodded and stood up. Immediately the others followed suit and, at a nudge from Tim, Amanda scrambled to her feet as well.

'I think we've set the groundwork for our further discussion, gentlemen—and Miss Sutton,' said the Sheikh, inclining his head towards Amanda and smiling. 'Perhaps it would be wise to take a break for a few minutes. I don't know about the rest of you, but I could use a cup of coffee after all that dry talk!'

The assembled group laughed politely and murmured in agreement. The Sheikh pressed a button under the table, and great sliding doors at the far side of the room were thrown open, revealing a magnificently appointed lounge. There was a large round table in its centre, laden with a silver coffee service and plates of tiny, elaborate pastries. Amanda followed the rest of the group into the adjoining room, but she felt uncomfortable and out of place. Already, small groups had formed, and everyone, including Tim, seemed to be engrossed in conversation. Hoping to remain inconspicuous, Amanda drifted towards an alcove and began to examine several delicate paintings which hung there.

'Aren't you going to have some coffee, Miss Sutton?' Nicholas ben Saad had come up behind her as silently as a cat, and she turned abruptly, trying not to appear as startled as she felt.

'No, thank you, Your Excellency. I don't care for any,' she said quickly. His blue eyes were fixed upon her in the same inscrutable way she had noticed during the meeting. 'Have you any questions about the presentation?'

He smiled casually and took her arm, walking her further into the quiet seclusion of the alcove. 'No, none just yet. Actually, I was quite pleased with what I heard. You seem very well informed.'

'I think I am, sir—at least, I hope I am.' Taking a deep breath, Amanda stood still and turned to face him. 'Perhaps I shouldn't bring this up, but Mr Gamal seemed a little distressed when he met me yesterday. I just want to assure you that I'm really very good at what I do.'

His eyes flashed with sudden amusement and he smiled at her. 'I'm sure you are,' he said, and she blushed furiously.

'I meant that I'm very good at my job, Your Excellency. Just in case there was any question about my abilities.'

'Miss Sutton, I have ever confidence in your abilities. Why are you so defensive?'

'Why does everyone say——' Amanda bit back her words, amazed at how foolish she must sound. 'I'm terribly sorry, sir,' she apologised. 'Please forgive me. I seem to have been behaving rudely ever since I arrived.'

'There's nothing to forgive, Miss Sutton. I admire a woman who says what she thinks.' Suddenly he gestured towards the wall in front of them. 'What do you think of my paintings? They're quite beautiful, don't you agree?'

'Yes, they certainly are,' she answered, relieved at the change of subject. 'I'm afraid I don't know much about art. Are they by someone whose name I should know?'

He smiled and moved nearer to her. 'Not really,' he said, placing his hand in the small of her back and walking her further into the alcove. She was acutely aware of the steady, warm pressure of his fingers through the clinging silk dress. 'At least, they're not by anyone you'd know yet. I don't know much about art, either, except whether or not I like a particular piece. It pleases me to pick up paintings here and there in my travels. This one is my newest acquisition, and my favourite.' He pointed to a small, exquisite nude. The girl in the painting was quite beautiful, and defined in soft, glowing colours which accented her delicate sensuality. 'She looks a bit like you, doesn't she?'

Amanda could feel her face colouring. 'No, not really,' she answered stiffly. 'I don't see any resemblance at all.'

He took her gently by the shoulders and turned her towards him into the light, studying her intently. She tried to move away from him, but the pressure of his hands remained constant.

'I do,' he said with great certainty. 'The same colour eyes, the same fine bone-structure, the same soft skin tones.' His penetrating stare travelled slowly down her body and back to her face, and she felt as if he had somehow looked through her silk dress to the soft flesh beneath. 'Of course, I can only guess at any other similarity,' he added thoughtfully, smiling at her. 'You're somewhat more modestly dressed than she is.'

'I should hope so,' Amanda said stiffly, trying to control her irritation.

'Still,' he continued pleasantly, 'I must admit you puzzle me. I can understand modesty, but why would such a beautiful woman go to such great lengths to try and disguise that beauty? I would have thought it would be to a woman's advantage to capitalise on her looks if she wants to get ahead.'

'I don't know what kinds of women you've dealt with, but that isn't the sort I am or the sort I want to be,' she said quickly. 'And I don't think the way I look or the way I dress is any of your business.' She turned away, her body and voice taut with anger. 'There's no point in continuing this conversation, Your Excellency.'

'I'm glad to hear we're having a conversation. I thought for a moment there we were in the midst of an argument.' Nicholas ben Saad smiled, and his face mirrored the light amusement in his tone. 'And I don't think your employer would be happy to see us quarrelling, do you? No, don't turn around, Miss Sutton. I assure you, Mr Pauling keeps looking over here, and we wouldn't want to worry him, would we? Why don't you smile a bit—that's the way—and Tim will relax. There, you see, that wasn't so difficult, now was it?'

There was a dryness in Amanda's throat as she realised how badly she was handling this first encounter with her new client. What was wrong with her? If this man was determined to reduce her to a helpless, trembling female, he was certainly succeeding! She took a deep breath and tilted her chin up bravely.

'Your Excellency, I'm afraid we've got off to a bad start. Perhaps, in some way, it's my fault,' she said, hating herself for the necessary lie. 'Whatever the reason, I'd like to start over again. After all, we are going to be working together for quite some time.'

She held her breath while she waited for him to answer. Finally he moved closer to her and spoke quietly.

'You're right, Miss Sutton, and I accept your apology, but only on certain conditions. To begin with, I'd prefer that you call me Nick. As you say, we're going to be working together and there's no need for this continued formality. Can you manage that?'

She was all too aware of the gentle but compelling pressure of his hand on her shoulder. With difficulty, she managed to nod her head in agreement and smile slightly.

'Fine,' said Nick. His eyes narrowed and seemed to be drawing her into him. 'The second request is just as simple. Have dinner with me tonight, Amanda. I'll call for you at eight o'clock at your hotel.'

'Impossible,' she said at once. 'I have work to do.'

'At night? Tim assured me you were hardworking, but don't you think that's carrying things a bit too far?'

Amanda stepped away from him, moving from the touch of his hand, trying hard to keep a polite, impersonal smile on her face, although she knew he must be aware of her irritation.

'Hard work has got me where I am today, Your Excellency.'

'Nick,' he corrected gently. Abruptly, his voice lowered and became somehow menacing. 'And you can be back where you were in a minute, Amanda. All I have to do is tell Pauling that you're too busy with your personal life to devote the necessary time to this project. Shall I do that? He's coming in our direction right now.'

'This is blackmail!' she hissed, trembling with fury.

'It's a business deal, Amanda, and I'm known for driving hard bargains. You'd better decide quickly.'

'You win,' she said in panic. 'But I'll never forgive you for this, never.'

Nick grinned at her just as Tim came up beside them.

'Is everything all right, Nick?' he asked, looking from the Sheikh to Amanda's pale face. 'You two seemed to be deep in talk.'

'Miss Sutton was just telling me that she'd never forgive me if I don't meet her this evening and go over some ideas she has. I admit, Tim, I'm impressed. She's not only lovely, she's as dedicated to her work as I am.'

'I told you she was terrific,' Tim said enthusiastically, and patted Amanda on the back. 'Just don't let her take advantage of you.'

'Don't worry about that—I always manage to keep my employees in line!'

Both men laughed goodnaturedly, and Amanda managed a weak smile. She excused herself and returned to the conference-room, where she made a pretence of reviewing her notes. In actuality, she was seething with anger and humiliation, although it wasn't as if she hadn't come up against this sort of situation before. Since her divorce, occasionally she had met men who thought nothing of making passes at her, but she had either walked away in disgust or turned them aside with cool detachment. She couldn't very well walk away from this man who was her client, not unless she wanted to give up her job. And when she had tried to brush him aside politely, he had all but threatened her. She glanced down at her tailored shirtwaister dress and sighed. The clothes she so carefully wore, the severe hairstyle, the understate make-up, all the outward armour she used to camouflage herself, had served her well, until now. For a wild moment she thought of complaining to Tim, but she discarded that desperate idea quickly. He would only be convinced that she really was the liability he expected her to be or, worse still, he would wink and tell her to make the most of the influence on Nick.

She gritted her teeth as the Sheikh entered the room and smiled in her direction. The man was an arrogant, overbearing despot, she thought bitterly, but she'd survive somehow. She always had.

The balance of the meeting passed without incident. The men split into small groups and Amanda joined several bankers who wanted to discuss the costs of the forthcoming project. From time to time, she felt as if Nick was looking at her, but she kept her attention on the papers in front of her. When the conference ended, he shook her hand politely and reminded her of their evening appointment. As if she could forget! she thought.

'Let's walk to the office,' Tim suggested once they had reached the street. 'It's only a couple of blocks from here.'

Amanda agreed instantly, hoping she could walk off some of her angry energy, but it was impossible to do so. Tim kept talking excitedly about the meeting and Nick.

'He's really impressed with you, Sutton. And I have to admit that I am, too. I'd have thought you'd be too tired to meet with him tonight, but you're a real go-getter. I think you've got him eating out of your hand.'

Or biting at it, she thought grimly, but she forced herself to smile in agreement.

'Yes, things seem to have gone well today. Tim, I have a suggestion. Why don't you join us tonight? I'm sure Nick would appreciate your input.'

He scratched his head and frowned. 'I wish I could, but I can't make it. I made an appointment with one of those bankers to go over some projected cost runs. Tell you what, though—I'll join you for coffee, say around ten o'clock, if you think it's a good idea.'

'Oh, I think it's a great idea,' she said happily. 'I just know the Sheikh will be delighted.'

Amanda spent the balance of the day organising her desk and becoming familiar with the staff at the Olsen & Tibbs branch office. She dipped into the stack of reports and figures that had already come in from the desert site, losing herself in finding solutions to problems and equations. A minor error in a flow chart caught her attention and she corrected it quickly, pencilling in a note to the crew chief at the site. It wasn't anything enormous, she knew, but the change she had made would save the company time and money. This was what she was here for, she thought, leaning back and stretching her aching muscles. This was why she was in Morocco, and the sooner Nicholas ben Saad understood that, the better.

Back at her hotel, peering into the closet, she smiled as she thought of the way in which she had involved Tim in the evening's plans. It would be worth suffering through dinner with the Sheikh, just to see his face when his uninvited guest joined them. Deliberately, she pushed aside the few soft, flattering things she had brought along and chose a dark cotton dress with long sleeves and a demure collar. She brushed her hair into its usual chignon, not even bothering to add a touch of lipstick to her mouth. A glance in the mirror assured her that she looked exactly as she had intended: well groomed, efficient, but not particularly attractive. Two could play at this game, she thought grimly, and she wasn't a novice.

Promptly at ten to eight, Amanda locked the door behind her and went down to the lobby. It was crowded with guests on their way out for the evening, but she saw Nick at once, striding across the carpet from the front door, elegantly dressed in a dark grey suit and moving with an easy animal grace. He smiled when he saw her, and for a brief second she almost regretted that she hadn't worn something softer and prettier.

'I might have known you'd be prompt, Amanda,' he said softly, taking her hand in his and lifting it to his lips. 'Or were you afraid of letting me come up to your room to call for you?'

'I thought it would save time if I met you here, Your Ex. . .Nick,' she said stiffly, correcting herself before he could.

He smiled and tucked her hand into the crook of his arm. 'I'm all for that. I've made reservations for us in a little French place across town, and it will take us a while to get there. I think you'll like it.'

Amanda sighed and shrugged her shoulders. 'I'm sure I would, but I really hoped we could dine here at the hotel. All the guide books I read recommended this place, and I'd love to find out if they're right. Would that be all right with you?'

Nick hesitated briefly. She could sense his disappointment but, as she had expected, her request had been made so pleasantly that he couldn't very well turn her down.

'Of course,' he said. 'Whatever you prefer.'

The hotel restaurant was dimly lit and handsome. Designed along the lines of a European café, its soft lighting and intimate seating arrangements were not what she had anticipated, and she regretted not having looked the place over earlier. The head waiter showed them to a secluded table along the wall, and as she settled into her chair, she casually moved it further from Nick's. Nick ordered wine for both of them and the sommelier served it with a flourish.

'To the first of many evenings together,' said Nick, touching his glass to hers. He sipped at the delicate white wine and smiled at her. 'I hope you like wine, Amanda. The Frenchman in me would rebel without it at dinner. You look beautiful—did I tell you that?'

Amanda felt a rush of colour to her cheeks. 'That's very gallant, and very French,' she said coolly, 'but not true. I'm not really dressed for this place, but since this is a dinner meeting between employer and employee I didn't think it was necessary.'

Nick leaned across the tiny table and grinned at her. 'Is that how it's going to be, Amanda? Well, that's all right; after all, we're going to be working together, aren't we? I think we should get to know each other better. Strictly in the interest of good business practices, of course,' he added in an innocent tone.

She raised her eyes to his, but she could read nothing in their blue depths. 'If you insist,' she said, 'although I doubt if we're really going to be doing much together. Much work, I mean,' she added swiftly, blushing at the sound of her own words. 'I'll be doing most of my work in my office.'

Nick nodded and smiled. 'You've already begun, I hear,' he said, pouring more wine into her glass before she could protest. 'Tim tells me you caught an error in one of our flow charts this afternoon.'

'It wasn't much,' Amanda said in some surprise. 'Just a minor miscalculation, really. I didn't think you'd know about it.'

'You mean you didn't think I'd understand it, don't you? I put in a few years at a desk, Amanda, and I still like to keep my hand in. Does that surprise you?'

'No,' she said quickly, 'not really. Well, a little, perhaps. I mean, you seemed quite knowledgeable at today's meeting, but I thought. . .I guess I just assumed. . .'

She paused in sudden confusion, and Nick's eyes seemed to sparkle at some hidden jest.

'Never assume anything, Amanda, at least, not about me. And I'm sure I know what you thought—that my engineering staff wrote my proposal for me.'

'Your Excellency. . .'

He grinned at her and shook his head. 'Nick,' he

corrected gently. 'Surely a woman who can read a flow chart can remember something so simple as a name?'

She took a deep breath and folded her hands tightly in her lap. 'Nick, I didn't mean to imply that you didn't understand my job. It's just that. . .'

'It's just that not everything about me is in your client profile,' he finished for her pleasantly. 'That's exactly what I suggested when I said we should get to know each other better. Now, don't you think that might be a good idea?'

'I guess it might be helpful,' she admitted at last, a faint smile playing at the corners of her mouth. 'Especially now that I know you're going to be checking up on my work.'

The teasing smile faded from his face. 'That isn't what I'm going to be doing at all,' he said quietly. 'After all, Amanda, I'm about to entrust a major project, a very important project, to you, and I wouldn't do that unless I had every confidence in your abilities.' He leaned back in his chair and smiled slightly. 'Surely you didn't think you were the only one who did some background research on the people you'd be working with on this project?'

'I didn't do anything of the sort,' Amanda said stiffly. 'The firm always gives us helpful information on new clients.'

'It couldn't have been terribly precise information, Amanda,' Nick said gently, 'or you wouldn't have been ready to try and dismiss me so easily.'

'That's not what I did at all. It's just that I think it's important to establish the. . .the right kind of professional relationship, right from the start. What I mean is. . .'

A smile lit his handsome face and he held up his hand. 'You don't have to explain, Amanda—I know precisely what you meant. You want me to ignore the fact that my new employee is not only a competent engineer, but also a lovely woman. Or did you think I wouldn't see the woman hiding behind that careful disguise?' he asked, his eyes raking casually over her.

'And now we're right back to where we were this afternoon,' she said angrily, colour rushing to her cheeks. 'I don't have to explain myself to you. Only the way I do my job is your concern.'

'I'm not concerned,' Nick said pleasantly, 'only curious. I get the feeling that the real Amanda Sutton is hiding inside that carefully cultivated, efficient image you show the world, waiting for the right man to set her free.'

She drew a sharp breath and placed her trembling hands on the table's edge. 'Is that what you think, Your Excellency?' she asked coldly, fighting back the rage within her. 'Well, you're very wrong. I am precisely what you see, in spite of what your. . .your overblown male ego wants you to believe. I'm a woman—a person— who's worked very hard to get where I am, and I certainly don't need a man to set me free, whatever that means.'

Nick shrugged and smiled, his eyes never leaving her face. 'Oh, I think you know what it means, Amanda. Surely you'll admit there's more to life than just doing your job.'

'It's not a job,' she snapped. 'It's a career, Your Excellency, and I'm quite serious about it.'

'I'm sure you are.'

'And please don't patronise me,' she added quickly. 'If I were a man, you'd never question my dedication to my work, would you?'

There was a long pause. His eyes narrowed and he stared at her thoughtfully while she forced herself to look

back at him. At last, he smiled ruefully and lifted his
wineglass to her in a mock salute.

'*Touché*,' he drawled. 'You're right, of course. I
wouldn't.'

She was surprised and a bit flustered at the honesty of
his response. 'Well then,' she said quietly, 'I've made my
point, haven't I?'

'Still,' he added carefully, sipping at his wine, 'if you
were a man. . .'

Her head rose defiantly and she stared at him. 'If I
were a man. . .what?'

Nick burst out laughing. 'If you were a man, we'd
both be in a rather awkward situation right now,
wouldn't we?'

In spite of herself, she began to smile. 'But the whole
situation wouldn't have developed, would it? Your
Excellency—Nick—I really would like to stay on here
and do my job, and I'm certain I'd do it well. But if it's
impossible for me to do so, if you can't work with me,
with a woman. . .'

His eyebrows arched in surprise. 'Have I said that?'

'No,' she admitted reluctantly, 'but if it's going to be a
problem, Olsen & Tibbs will replace me—at your
request, of course.'

'I have no intention of making such a request,
Amanda. I told you earlier, I'm sure you're well qualified
for this project.'

'Thank you,' she said formally.

'You're welcome,' he answered, and then a mischievous grin lit his face. 'Besides, I've seen too many
other engineers to want to replace you. They come in all
shapes and sizes, and I'd be a fool to run the risk of
trading you for some fellow with a fat cigar and five
o'clock shadow. I'm not trying to embarrass you,' he
added quickly, 'I'm just being honest. You can't fault

me for that, can you?'

'Just so long as we understand each other,' said Amanda, pushing back her chair and beginning to get to her feet.

Nick frowned and touched her hand. 'Where are you going?'

'Well, I thought—I thought. . .now that we've come to an understanding. . .I mean, now that you know I don't want to. . .that I'm not. . .' Her words drifted off into an uncomfortable silence, and Nick grinned.

'You thought I arranged this evening so I could seduce you, or coerce you into my bed.'

'Not exactly,' she mumbled miserably, all too aware of the steadiness of his gaze and the light pressure of his hand on hers.

'Actually, the thought of making love to you did cross my mind,' he admitted lightly, then he smiled. 'But I've never forced myself upon a woman, no matter what you may think.'

'I didn't think that,' she said quickly.

'I hope not, Amanda. I don't play the part of a villain very well. Anyway,' he added, taking his hand from hers and giving her the menu, 'now that we understand each other, why don't we declare a truce?'

Amanda shifted uncomfortably in her chair. 'I'm perfectly willing to do that.'

Nick opened the elaborate menu and looked at it for a minute. 'Actually, I'm in no rush,' he said, his voice low and casual. 'I can wait, if that's what you prefer.'

She could feel her cheeks reddening and she stared at him. 'What did you say?' she asked faintly.

His face was a study in innocent charm. 'I said, I'm in no rush for dinner, Amanda. Or are you ready to order now?' When she didn't respond, he turned and signalled for the waiter. 'Shall I order for both of us?' he asked, and she nodded in agreement, somehow not quite certain they'd been talking about the same thing at all.

Amanda watched him as he ordered a series of exotic dishes from the attentive waiter, studying the planes and angles of his face, trying to make some sense out of this man who always seemed not quite what she expected. Gradually, as they made inconsequential small talk about the weather, the desert project, the difficulties of jet lag, she began to relax.

I hope you like artichokes,' said Nick when their first course was served. 'Perhaps I should have asked you.'

'Oh, I love them,' she said quickly. 'I'm not that provincial.' A faint smile played at the corners of her mouth. 'Actually, I guess I am. I practically grew up on artichokes; in southern California, it's almost against the law not to eat them. But I've never seen one stuffed before.'

Nick grinned and picked up his salad fork. 'Then you're in for a treat. If it's possible to make a good thing better, this is the way to do it.' He waited until she had tasted the artichoke and smiled her approval. 'Is that where you're from? Southern California? Los Angeles, I'll bet.'

'No, not quite,' she laughed. 'I grew up in a little town you never heard of—Santa Margarita. Just a downtown area you could fit into this dining-room and some sleepy streets lined with old houses.'

'You left out that little auto parts shop on—what is it—? Hammer Road, I think.' He chuckled at the surprised look on Amanda's face. 'Yes, I know the town. I've raced near there, at the track in Riverside, a number of times, and that little store has a lot of things my crew and I have needed at one time or another. I was there just a few months ago, as a matter of fact. I'll bet I drove right past your house.' He smiled and sipped at his wine. 'If I'd have known, I'd have stopped and introduced myself.'

'Impossible,' she said, too quickly. 'I haven't been back there in a long time.'

Nick waited while the waiter cleared the table and then arranged their trout amandine before them.

'Don't you go home to visit your family?' he asked then.

'There's just my mother,' Amanda answered, avoiding his eyes. 'And I've been too busy to go back.'

'Too busy working?'

'That's right,' she said, almost defiantly. 'I haven't had any time to spare.'

'That's too bad,' he said softly. She looked up quickly, but the expression on his face was unreadable. 'I've always thought it important to relax once in a while, get away from the pressures of business.'

'Is that why you race? To get away from business?'

Nick laughed and leaned back in his chair. 'You make that sound almost sinful, Amanda! But the answer is yes, that's part of the reason. I like the feeling I get from driving. It's a kind of harmonic discipline, if that makes any sense at all. You know, you have to get the car to its peak performance level, and then you have to know just how much to ask of it, and of yourself, until finally you get out on the track. Then, if you've hit the right balance—if all the conditions are right—it all blends together.'

She watched his face as he talked, unable to take her eyes from his. Although they were wide, with a disarming kind of almost boyish charm, they occasionally narrowed alarmingly to feral glints of indigo that seemed to transform him from French to Bedouin with fascinating ease. His thick, dark lashes were as black as his hair, and his long, straight nose was a handsome counterpoint to his sensual mouth. There was a hard, animal beauty about him; altogether, he gave the impression of re-pressed power. He was telling her about his cars and his pit crew, casually crediting them with his successes on the track, even making her laugh as he told her about some of his less satisfactory moments at a recent race. With a suddenness that was almost like a blow, she realised how long it had been since she had smiled at a man's jokes or enjoyed one's company, and something must have shown on her face, because Nick paused and laughed wryly.

'I must be boring you to death, Amanda. I didn't mean to go on quite that long.'

'No, I'm interested, really. I went to a couple of races at Riverside when I was in school, but it just seemed like a lot of cars zooming around in circles for hours at a time. I guess I never realised there was so much work and skill involved.'

'So there was a time in your life when you took time out for fun?' he teased. 'I can picture you then, you know, with your hair in a ponytail, and your white socks, and—what do you call them—those shoes with the coins in them?'

She tried not to smile, but it was impossible. 'Penny loafers,' she said, beginning to giggle. 'But that outfit's about thirty years out of date.'

Nick grinned and shrugged his shoulders. 'That's what comes of learning about American girls from watching old movies!'

'Well then, we're even—I half expect to see Humphrey Bogart and Ingrid Bergman come through those doors any minute. I like old movies, too. I sometimes think I'm the only person awake in New York at three in the morning, watching Clark Gable and Carole Lombard on my television set.'

'You must have been a strange teenager,' he said, his

eyes twinkling. 'Going to watch car races during the day, and staying up half the night to see old movies.'

Amanda laughed and shook her head. 'That's somebody else you're describing. I went to Riverside twice, with my Girl Scout troop, and my mother would have killed me if she found me watching television late at night. No, I wasn't like that at all.'

The smile faded from his face. 'I was only teasing you, Amanda. Actually, I'll bet you studied hard, and got good grades in all your subjects, and never took time to do anything frivolous.'

She stiffened defensively, but something in his voice and face made her finally sigh and nod her head. 'Almost one hundred per cent right,' she said lightly. 'Although I did do something out of character once. I saved my baby-sitting money, and then I cut my classes one day and spent all my money at a ranch outside town, riding an old horse named Prince. Well, after all,' she said quickly, when he started to grin, 'I'd learned to ride at Girl Scout camp, and I'd been seeing a lot of old Roy Rogers movies. . .'

'On late-night television?'

'On after-school television,' she said primly, and then even she smiled. 'It really doesn't sound very frivolous, does it?'

'It sounds like fun,' Nick said quickly. 'I used to ride a lot, when I was younger. Travelling through the desert on horseback is the only way to really get to know it. Would you like to come with me some time?'

'I don't think so,' she said quickly, feeling suddenly vulnerable and exposed. 'I'm sure I'll be too busy for that.'

'But you're working for me, Amanda,' he said pleasantly, 'and I'm not that hard a taskmaster. Although I'm not much of a host,' he added, reaching for the wine bottle. 'I forgot to refill your glass.'

She reached out her hand to stop him, and his fingers brushed against her wrist. Her skin felt as if it had been seared, and she snatched her hand away so quickly that Nick stared at her.

'Tell me about the paintings in your office,' she said hurriedly, to cover her confusion. 'They're beautiful.'

'I'm glad you liked them. That's my other great weakness, I suppose. It's almost impossible for me to resist adding something new to my collection.'

'It's not like racing, though, is it? I mean, collecting art seems so different from speeding around a track.'

Nick shook his head. 'There's beauty and subtlety in a fine machine, like my Porsche, as well as in art. It's all a matter of perspective, of looking below the surface. I guess I have a passion for collecting beautiful things, whether they're paintings, or sculpture, or fine cars.'

Or women, she thought suddenly, looking away from him. He was talking about his last trip to Paris, telling her about a dealer who had tried to sell him a fake Renoir, and she smiled at all the right moments, nodding her head as he talked, but her eyes were drawn again to his face, to the expressive gestures he made with his hands, and suddenly she wondered what it would be like to let those hands caress her body, to feel that arrogant-looking mouth on hers. The unbidden, unexpected images that flashed before her were so intense, so intimate, that a visible tremor passed through her.

'Are you all right, Amanda?' Nick asked immediately.

'Yes, I'm fine,' she said, hoping her voice sounded more assured than she felt. 'I suddenly felt a bit chilled, that's all. I guess I'm just a little tired.'

'Of course you are,' he said, signalling for the waiter. 'You're probably still exhausted from that long flight over and today's meeting. I'm sorry; I've been prattling on too long.'

'No, you haven't,' she said quickly, blushing slightly when he glanced at her in surprise. 'I mean, I've enjoyed talking with you, Nick.'

'Well,' he said, smiling at her, 'that's nice to hear. At least this hasn't been such a terrible evening for you, after all.'

'It's been very pleasant,' she admitted, looking down at the table.

'I'm glad, Amanda. I think I even caught you smiling once or twice. You ought to do that more often; you have a particularly lovely smile, you know. Don't look so uncomfortable,' he added when she frowned. 'That was just an honest statement of fact. Honesty is important in a relationship, especially between two people who are going to be working together, don't you agree?'

'Yes, of course,' she said slowly, feeling somehow as if she were losing ground.

'Well then, let's at least agree that we'll not only get to know each other better, but that we'll always be truthful.'

Amanda looked at him, searching his face for some hidden meaning, sensing a masked commitment within the simple words.

'That's not a complicated request, Amanda,' he said quietly. 'Why are you afraid of agreeing to it?'

'That's ridiculous,' she said quickly. 'I'm not afraid of anything.'

'Aren't you?' he asked softly, his eyes narrowing as they focused on hers with a sudden intensity.

She was struggling for the right answer, for the kind of careful, neutral response that she could hide behind, when she saw Tim Pauling standing in the doorway. Relief flooded through her.

'There's Tim,' she said quickly, waving at him. 'I asked him to join us for coffee—I was sure you wouldn't mind,' she added, almost casually.

Nick's mouth tightened. 'Did you think you'd need reinforcements, Amanda?' he grated through his teeth. 'At least you've answered my question. You are afraid.'

'I'm not,' she said in a desperate rush, watching Tim as he crossed the room towards them. 'What on earth would I be afraid of?'

'I know the answer to that, too,' Nick said quietly, just as Tim reached their table. 'And so do you.'

'So, how's it going, you two?' asked Tim, pulling up a chair. 'I hope your meeting went better than mine. Nick, your banker is a great guy, but he's only interested in the bottom line.'

'Sometimes that's all that's important,' said Nick, his eyes never leaving Amanda's face.

She stood so abruptly that her chair almost toppled over. 'No, don't get up, please,' she said as both men rose to their feet. 'Tim, would you mind terribly if I went to my room and left you two to talk without me? I've got a terrible headache, and I don't think I'd be very much help.'

'Of course, kid. It's been a long day. Nick and I can manage. I'll take you up, if you like.'

But Nick's hand was already on her arm. 'I'll see Amanda to her room, Tim,' he said easily. 'Why don't you order coffee and brandy for both of us?'

'This really isn't necessary,' she protested as Nick guided her through the dining-room, holding her arm as gently and firmly as if she were a bird that might somehow take flight. 'I'm perfectly capable of finding my own way.'

'I'm sure you are,' he agreed, as the elevator doors closed behind them. 'But we were in the midst of a conversation, and I didn't think you'd want to continue it in front of Tim.'

'What conversation?' The elevator doors slid open and she hurried past Nick to the door to her room. 'I don't know what you're talking about.'

'We were talking about honesty between us, and why you're so afraid of it,' he said, taking the room key from her fumbling fingers and turning her towards him. 'Surely you haven't forgotten?'

'I don't know what you mean,' she said quickly. 'And I'm tired of the way you keep insisting I'm afraid. Whatever this little word game of yours is, it's pointless. If you're trying to confuse me. . .'

'Is that what you think?' he demanded, almost angrily. He was so close to her that she could feel his warm breath fanning her hair, and she started to turn away, but he reached out and cupped her face in his hand, tilting her chin up until her eyes met his. 'This is no game, Amanda. Something is happening between us—don't shake your head that way; you can feel it as well as I can.' His fingers moved gently against her cheek and she bit her lip as some other feeling, something more real than the anger she felt, flooded through her. 'It's not really me you're afraid of, is it, Amanda?' he asked quietly. 'I think it's yourself you fear, and what will happen if all those feelings you've got under lock and key get out in the open, where you'll have to face them?'

'This is ridiculous,' she said steadily. 'We barely know each other. . .'

'But we will,' he said softly, his fingers tightening against her face. 'I want to know the woman hidden inside you, the woman I caught a glimpse of tonight. Why are you so fearful of admitting that you want that, too?' he asked, and suddenly he bent towards her and his mouth, warm and gentle, claimed hers. She wanted to pull free, to fight him, to deny the soft feeling of warmth radiating through her, but his hand held her to him until, as unexpectedly as it had begun, the kiss ended. 'Do we understand each other?' whispered Nick, letting go of her.

Amanda drew a ragged breath and forced herself to stare defiantly into his eyes. 'I certainly understand you,' she said, snatching the dangling key from his hand. 'And I'll tell you this: for a man who's so successful, so good at making judgements, you've made a poor one about me. Goodnight,' she said coldly, and unlocked the door.

'Goodnight, Amanda,' he said pleasantly. 'Pleasant dreams.'

She slammed the door shut as hard as she could, taking grim satisfaction in the loud noise it made in the quiet corridor.

'Pleasant dreams indeed,' she muttered angrily. 'I'll probably have nightmares!' She stormed around the room, kicking her shoes into the corner and tossing her clothing on the floor as she undressed, tense with anger. He was an insufferable, egotistical animal, she raged to herself. Under that charming veneer lurked the same old enemy. She'd just have to find a way to deal with him.

And yet, when she finally fell asleep, after hours of useless trying, she did indeed dream, and her dreams were filled with shadowy images of Nick and the memory of the warm, sweet touch of his mouth on hers.

CHAPTER THREE

THE DAYS passed quickly, filled from morning to night
with meetings and deadlines. Amanda's work was
demanding and challenging, and as she became more and
more involved in the problems and specifications of the
developing project her lingering anger at Nick began to
fade in a growing respect for the scope and imagination of
his desert proposal. In fact, although at first she had felt a
momentary panic each time her phone rang, half
expecting it would be Nick calling, she began to wonder
when she would hear his voice again. The faint realisation that she wanted to was so confusing and disconcert-
ing that she shunted it aside like a ghostly spectre half
seen in the night.

There was precious little time to spend sightseeing,
but often she ate a quick lunch of yoghurt and fruit at her
desk just so she would have a half-hour or so to stroll the
streets of the city, blending into the crowds and enjoying
the wide, palm-lined main boulevards and winding,
narrow side streets of the Moroccan bazaars. The main
streets reminded her of all the pictures she had seen of
the handsome boulevards of Paris; they were filled with
outdoor cafés and well dressed, cosmopolitan crowds.
But the little side-streets held the true spirit of exotic
Morocco, where shopkeepers hawked their wares under
the very noses of the passers-by, and the smells of
cinnamon, clove, citrus, and sandalwood mingled
together in a unique and delicate perfume that was like
nothing she had ever experienced before. Occasionally
she lingered at a display of silver jewellery or hand-tooled

47

leather, but invariably she sighed regretfully and shook
her head when the shopkeepers approached her. She
gazed with longing at the graceful caftans woven from
linen, silk, or finely spun wool, but they all seemed an
expensive luxury for someone who, each evening,
returned wearily to an empty and lonely hotel room.

She was hurrying back to the office one afternoon
when an especially lovely dark blue caftan shot through
with silver caught her eye, and she paused to admire
it.

'Beautiful, isn't it? But a lighter colour would be cooler
to wear, I should think,' a deep voice behind her said
quietly.

Amanda turned slowly and stared at Nick. 'What are
you doing here?' she asked, regretting the triteness of the
words even as she uttered them.

He grinned and shrugged his shoulders. 'The same
thing you are,' he said. 'Window-shopping, enjoying the
bazaars. . . what is it you Americans call it? Playing the
hook?'

She tried not to smile, then she burst out laughing.
'Playing hookey,' she corrected. 'I think that's the
expression you're looking for.'

He smiled at her. 'Colloquial English isn't taught in
French boarding-schools, nor at Oxford,' he admitted.
'Anyway, what it comes down to is that I've stolen out of
my office for an hour or two. I'm surprised to see that
you've done the same thing.'

'Oh, I have to get back,' she said quickly, glancing at
her watch. 'My lunch-hour is just about over.'

A heavy woman, trailed by several small children,
pushed past them in the narrow confines of the street,
and Nick took Amanda's arm and guided her out of the
way of hurrying pedestrians.

'Mine has just started,' he said, walking her along the

cobblestoned gutter to the other side of the street. 'Won't you join me?'

'No, thank you. I told you, I have to get back. Anyway, I've already eaten.'

'Yoghurt and an apple,' he said with a disapproving frown. 'That's hardly what I call lunch.'

She drew to a halt and stared at him. 'How did you know that?' she demanded.

Nick smiled mysteriously, a hint of the inscrutable Bedouin on his lips. 'Don't stand still in the middle of the pavement, Amanda,' he said pleasantly, taking her arm again and moving her along with him. 'This crowd will simply walk right through you. Besides, what's the difference how I know it? It's true, isn't it?'

'Yes,' she admitted reluctantly, glancing up at him. 'Nick, I've got to get back.'

'Why?' he asked innocently. 'Will Tim be angry if you're late?'

'No, of course not. But I've got work to do. . .'

'Because, if you think you might need one, I'll give you a note to show him. Something along the lines of, "Please excuse Amanda for coming back late from lunch. She was kidnapped by a dangerous Bedouin." I'm always dangerous when I'm hungry,' he added, looking down at her, and she began to smile.

'Well, perhaps I'll just take five minutes for some coffee,' she said slowly. 'Actually, I'd like to ask you a question about the pipes we ordered for the pumping stations. . .'

'You're going to have a full Moroccan meal, young lady,' he said firmly, turning down another side street, 'and you'll be too busy enjoying it to talk business.'

Amanda started to protest, but he airily waved her aside as he stopped before a large charcoal brazier and bowed politely to the tiny, veiled old woman squatting behind it. She looked up, squealed in delight, and kissed his hand. Nick removed his hand from her grasp in obvious discomfort and grinned at Amanda apologetically.

'You can see that the ladies love me,' he drawled, and she giggled. He spoke some rapid Arabic words to the old woman, who looked at Amanda and smiled and nodded. Then she took two long wooden skewers from the brazier's grill, wrapped them and their contents in a large piece of oiled paper and handed the package to Nick, whispering to him and pointing at Amanda. He bowed again, handed her some silver coins, then he turned to Amanda.

'Smile prettily and say goodbye to her,' he said. 'She says you're very beautiful.'

She coloured slightly as she did what Nick had asked. 'Well, that's very nice of her. . .'

'She also said you need to gain at least forty pounds, and that she hopes you'll recover from your illness soon.'

'What?' she gasped indignantly, hurrying to keep up with his long strides.

'She thinks that's why you're so thin and pale,' he laughed, pausing at another street stall.

Amanda watched as he again bowed to the vendor, and yet another package of strange-looking food was deposited into Nick's outstretched hands. Eventually, as they wound their way deeper and deeper into the winding streets, into areas of the city where she had never been, she gave up counting the number of times they stopped and the number of packages each of them now held. Finally they emerged into a quiet, sun-dappled wide alley, miraculously free of people and shops.

'Where on earth are we?' asked Amanda, looking about her. 'I don't think I've ever been this lost!'

'We're going to a perfect place for lunch,' Nick assured her. 'It's just a few more metres.'

Slowly she followed him to an old iron gate, but when he pushed it open, she paused. 'Where are we going?' she asked suspiciously, looking at the shadowed lines of a house barely visible behind a growth of grapevines and palm trees.

'Trust me, Amanda,' he urged. 'It's not far now.'

'Whose house is that?' she asked, following him slowly through the gate. 'Is it yours?'

'Yes, but I don't use it very often, and I'm not planning to use it today,' he added quickly, smiling at her. 'I thought we'd eat lunch here, in the courtyard. Don't you think it's the perfect place for a picnic?'

They had entered a tiled enclosure, completely surrounded by the lush colours of a dozen varieties of native flowers, shaded by several sentry palms. Tiny birds flitted among the vines, their bright colours even more vivid than those of the flowers.

'It's lovely,' whispered Amanda. 'I can't believe a place like this exists so near those busy streets.'

Nick pulled off his jacket and loosened his tie. 'Sit down, Amanda,' he said, gesturing to a low marble bench. 'You're about to enjoy my idea of a feast.' Quickly he began to unwrap all the packages they had been carrying, laying them on an inlaid table next to the bench.

'We'll never eat all that!' she laughed, gazing in awe at the mounds of strange-looking foods. 'What is this stuff, anyway?'

'This is *sis kebabi*, what you call shish kebab,' he said, handing her a dripping skewer. 'Lamb, and mushrooms, and whatever else was fresh in the market this morning. And these are chick peas, and this is aubergine, and there's dates, and halva, and ripe figs, and these are little grilled fish—I don't know what you call them in English—but it's all delicious, I promise. It's going to be messy,' he warned, laughing as she gingerly picked up a skewer of lamb.

Amanda licked her fingers and nodded. 'Messy, but everything tastes wonderful. You were right; it's delicious. I've never had anything like this before.'

'Ah, Miss Sutton,' Nick said smoothly, 'zat ees because you have not had ze real Moroccan guide with you, no? Here, watch it, Amanda. You don't want to let that stuff drip on to your dress.' He leaned over and gently wiped the corner of her mouth with his handkerchief.

She nodded gratefully. 'Thank you. I guess there isn't a neat way to do this, is there?'

'No,' he agreed, smiling back at her. 'But that's part of the fun of a picnic, isn't it?'

Amanda nodded again, her mouth filled with the sticky sweetness of halva. 'Absolutely. I'd forgotten how great picnics can be. It's years since I've been on one.'

'No time for it?' Nick asked gently.

'I guess that's part of it,' she admitted slowly. 'And I don't know anybody in New York who'd want to do this kind of thing.' She smiled slightly and shrugged her shoulders. 'Actually, I don't know too many people in New York, when you come right down to it.'

'No time for that, either?'

'I'm not quite the stick-in-the-mud you make me out to be, Nick,' she said quickly. 'It's just that I had to keep my priorities straight.'

'I'm sure it hasn't been easy for you, Amanda, getting ahead in your field.' Nick paused while he unwrapped his last purchase, a bottle of French wine he had asked the vendor to uncork. 'While we're on the subject,' he added, glancing at her, 'I meant what I said the other night. I do think you're right for this job.'

'Thank you,' she said softly, smiling at him.

'I meant the rest of it, too. About us, I mean. Something brought us together—don't be afraid of it, just accept it.'

The sunwarmed date she had been eating seemed suddenly to catch in her throat. 'Nick, please, let's not start that again. I've forgotten that whole conversation.'

He reached over and gently brushed a bit of date from her mouth with his fingertip, and his hand lingered against the warmth of her skin.

'Have you?' he asked softly.

The bright blue of the afternoon sky seemed to be trapped in the blue of his eyes, and she fumbled for an answer, conscious of the sudden rapid beating of her heart. Suddenly something soft brushed against her leg and she gasped. Nick laughed and snatched up a small black kitten.

'It's all right,' he said. 'It's only Tiki, come to say hello. He belongs to the family that takes care of this place for me.'

'Oh, he's adorable,' smiled Amanda, stroking the kitten's glossy fur. 'I've always loved cats.'

'Yes, they're special, aren't they? All soft purrs one minute, and sharp claws the next. This one loves to play, don't you, Tiki?'

Amanda watched, entranced, while Nick took a string from one of the packages and dangled it in front of the kitten. It wiggled its sturdy body and then pounced on the string, wrapping it around its paws and getting itself completely enmeshed. She laughed as the kitten worked furiously to free itself, only to turn and attack the string again. It occurred to her that this Nick, tieless and relaxed, his lunch forgotten in the pleasure of the game, was not the same man who had so confused her in his office, nor even the same one she had had dinner with just a few nights before. He wasn't easy to categorise, or at least he didn't fit neatly into the mould she had tried to assign to him. She watched as he gently disengaged the kitten's sharp claws from his finely made linen shirt, laughing as Tiki batted at Nick's fingers.

He looked at her and grinned. 'He's a tough little thing, isn't he? He reminds me of a cat I had when I was a boy.'

'That must have been fun,' she said, 'having a cat to play with. I always wanted a pet when I was little.'

'You mean you didn't have one? I thought that was part of a typical American upbringing—you know, two-point-five children and one-point-five pets per family.'

Amanda shook her head and laughed. 'Now who's making assumptions?' she teased. 'No, no pets, and no brothers or sisters, either. My mother thinks animals are a nuisance. And my husband—my former husband— thought they just tied people down.'

The kitten's eyes closed in pleasure as Nick stroked its dark fur. 'Anything worth having is worth being tied to,' he said after a moment, and Amanda nodded in agreement.

'Sometimes I think about getting myself a cat. . .'

'And?' Nick prompted gently, looking at her.

She thought of the lonely women she saw on the streets of New York, walking their tiny dogs, carrying their pampered cats through Central Park, talking to their pets, cherishing them as if they were people, as if they could fill their empty lives, and her lips tightened.

'And they take up too much time,' she said briskly, standing up and brushing the crumbs from her skirt. 'It's late, Nick. I have to get back to the office.'

'But we haven't had our wine yet, Amanda. And I wanted to show you the formal gardens behind the house.'

'I can't spare the time, Nick. Really,' she added softly,

'I. . .I wish I could, but I have to get back.'

'Even if I give you that note I offered?' he asked, smiling at her.

'Even your note can't help me,' she laughed, smoothing down her skirt. 'There are cost runs that Tim's been waiting for, and I've got to do them this afternoon.' She watched as Nick placed the kitten on the ground, then she bent and stroked its fur. The kitten butted his head against her hand and she smiled. 'He likes to be petted, doesn't he?'

'He likes you,' Nick answered softly. 'Why wouldn't he? Tiki may be a cat, but he's not a fool.'

Their eyes caught and held briefly, then Amanda turned away. 'Nick,' she said hesitantly, 'I. . .I've really enjoyed our picnic. Thank you for a lovely afternoon.'

'It's I who should thank you,' he said. He was standing so close to her that she turned away, closing her eyes briefly as his cool fingers touched her arm lightly. 'Perhaps we could have lunch together again tomorrow.'

'I don't think so,' she said quickly. 'I have a busy day planned.'

'Then how about dinner tonight? Tomorrow night?' he added, when she shook her head.

'I can't, really, I'm. . .'

'Too busy, I know,' he said, opening the gate for her. 'Well, perhaps I'll find a way to change your mind, Amanda. After all, you can't avoid me for ever.'

'That's not what I'm doing,' she said.

'Isn't it?' he asked, as they began to walk back through the narrow streets.

Instead of answering, Amanda began to question him about the shops they passed and the veiled women doing their marketing at the open stalls that lined the streets. He talked with animation and obvious affection about his country and his people, until at last they reached the corner where they had met earlier. Amanda turned and held out her hand.

'Goodbye, Nick. Thank you for lunch.'

He smiled and raised her hand to his lips. 'Not goodbye, Amanda. *Au revoir*—until we meet again.'

She muttered a reply and then hurried across the street towards her office, almost grateful for the press of business that awaited her.

Memories of the picnic stayed with her for the next few days. In some ways, the afternoon had been more disquieting than their evening together. Amanda wondered if Nick would phone, if he would ask her out again, but he didn't, and she began to think that he had finally accepted her refusal as final. The thought gave her less pleasure than it once would have. It wasn't easy to admit, but she had enjoyed the time she spent with him, even though she hadn't expected to. He was funny, and relaxed, and good company. She knew no one like him, no one who could order an impeccable meal in an elaborate restaurant at night and yet enjoy an impromptu picnic in a sunny garden in the very midst of a busy day. And he was interested in her, in spite of the fact that she wouldn't let him get close to her. That, too, was a surprise; the few men she had dated since her divorce had seemed only interested in either a quick conquest or a sympathetic listener, one to whom they could tell their corporate troubles or their personal woes. But there was little time to assess her feelings and impressions; the initial stages of the desert project were moving towards completion, and it seemed as if each passing day brought Tim into her office with yet another problem to solve. When, one rushed and hot afternoon, he burst through the door and cleared his throat, she looked up expectantly.

'What now?' she asked wearily. 'I haven't finished

working out this morning's figures yet, Tim, so unless this is a really serious problem it'll just have to wait.'

'Problem? Who's got a problem, kid?' he asked happily. 'They just finished pouring the foundation for the last pump station. The new specs were approved, and it looks like we may even come in ahead of schedule.'

Amanda sighed and leaned back in her chair. 'That's great, Tim. I guess we can all begin to relax a little.'

'Relaxation is the order of the day, kid. We're going to start by celebrating tonight. I hope you brought something smashing to wear.'

'Don't tell me you're going to flatten the expense account and take me to a decent restaurant! I'd almost gotten used to eating dinner here at the office out of a brown paper bag.'

Tim walked across the room to the window. 'See those hills just outside the city? Well, if you look really hard, you can spot a white house in a stand of cypress. That's where we're celebrating,' he said triumphantly. 'In the Sheikh's town house.'

Amanda leaned forward and stared at Tim, who was grinning from ear to ear. 'You're kidding,' she said, but he shook his head and tapped the windowpane emphatically.

'Nope, I'm dead serious. You and I are invited to some private bash up there tonight. Most of the wheelers and dealers we met the first day will be there, along with a bunch of other people. This ought to be something to write home about, Sutton. This guy is supposed to have a gorgeous home and a spectacular art collection. So just leave here early, and put on your fanciest, classiest gown. . .'

'I don't even own anything like that, Tim,' she said quickly. 'Why don't you just make my apologies for me, and then tomorrow you can tell me all about it?'

'Sutton,' Tim said patiently, 'I don't think you quite understand the situation. This is kind of like a royal command. Well, maybe that's a little bit exaggerated, but there's no choice about going. This party is for us. After all, we represent Olsen & Tibbs, don't we?'

'Yes, of course, Tim, but I can't. . .'

'But you can and you will, kid,' he said. 'And if you really don't have something to wear, why don't you finish up whatever's on your desk and then leave? There's some kind of dress shop in the hotel, isn't there?'

'Yes, there is, but. . .'

'That's an order, kid. Beside,' he added, winking at her, 'what's so terrible about spending a few hours in a beautiful house, rubbing shoulders with the jet-set, surrounded by luxury? What have you got to do that's better than that? Wash your hair?'

Amanda burst out laughing in spite of herself. 'When you put it like that, I guess it does sound foolish. OK, I give in. What time shall I be ready?'

Tim grinned and punched her lightly on the arm. 'That's the ticket, kid! Be ready at eight o'clock sharp. And I meant what I said about dressing up tonight. It should be a kind of formal evening. And who knows?' he added, just before he closed the door on his way out of her office, 'You just might have a good time.'

Who knows, indeed? Amanda thought suddenly. She just might.

CHAPTER FOUR

'YOU WERE wrong,' Amanda whispered softly to Tim that evening as they stood in the foyer of Nick's town house. 'You said this was going to be a formal evening. You should have said "elegant".'

Tim nodded in agreement. 'Well,' he muttered, 'at least it's a little smaller than Versailles.'

She forced a faint smile to her lips as she looked around the sculpture-lined room, almost wishing she had refused to come along. She glanced down at her dress, wondering if it was suitable. She had done as Tim had suggested and gone to the boutique in the hotel, where, after what seemed hours of indecision, she had finally given in to the chic saleswoman and purchased a long, shimmering white silk gown. Its clinging fabric moulded itself to every inch of her body, accentuating her high breasts, slender waist, and softly curved hips. Only the thinnest of straps kept the dress on her shoulders, and in a desperate effort at modesty, she had draped a filmy blue chiffon scarf around herself. The gown's long, tapered skirt was slit up one side, and she was uncomfortably aware of the way her long legs flashed each time she moved. She had combed and re-combed her long hair, unsure of how it looked best, until finally she had simply pinned it high on top of her head, although a few wispy golden tendrils were already curling down the nape of her neck. Her thick, dark lashes needed nothing to enhance them, and she knew her cheeks were flushed enough without blusher.

Tim had seemed startled at the sight of her. 'You look

terrific,' he had finally said after a long silence, and she hadn't known whether to be pleased or not. Now, walking up a dramatic marble staircase, she felt suddenly vulnerable and conspicuous. Sounds of music and laughter drifted towards them from open double doors.

'Nice homey little place, isn't it?' murmured Tim as they entered the main salon.

The room was enormous, richly carpeted in magnificent Oriental rugs. The walls were hung with rare paintings Amanda had only seen copies of before. Crystal chandeliers hung gleaming from the ceiling, and everywhere she looked there were clusters of elegantly dressed people. Although she suspected that some of the women's gowns had cost more than her entire wardrobe, Amanda was relieved to note that her white silk dress was at least able to hold its own.

'Sutton, I just saw one of the accountants Nick had with him in New York when we closed the deal last fall. You won't mind if I pop over to have a few words with him, will you?' Without giving her time to answer, Tim smiled and shook his head ruefully. 'I keep forgetting, that's one of the good things about you, kid—you're not the clinging vine type. Now, if you were like my wife, I'd have to stick to your side all night.'

Amanda forced herself to smile brightly, although she wanted to beg him not to leave her. The sight of all these strangers and the glittering surroundings was making her nervous; added to that was the knowledge that, sooner or later, she would have to come face to face with Nick. She watched enviously while Tim melted into a nearby group, then took a glass of white wine from a passing waiter and edged towards a delicate wire sculpture balanced on a glass-topped table.

'Good evening, Amanda. I told you we'd see each other again, didn't I?'

She turned slowly and looked at Nick. 'You did, didn't you?' she said pleasantly. 'I just never thought you'd go to all this trouble to arrange it.'

He laughed with delight. 'I wish I could take credit for such a clever scheme, but this party was planned long ago.' For the briefest moment, something replaced the glint of amusement in his eyes. 'Still, I'd probably have come to this sooner or later, if that's what it takes to get you to spend the evening with me.' His gaze swept over her. 'You look lovely, Amanda,' he said softly. 'Even more beautiful than I remembered.'

'I. . .I was just admiring this piece of sculpture,' she said unevenly, pulling the chiffon scarf more tightly around her. 'It's very handsome.'

'Yes, it is, isn't it? It's a fairly new piece, something I picked up at a little gallery in London. I have some other things by the same sculptor you'd probably like as well.'

'I noticed those figures in the foyer when Tim and I came in. They're wonderful.'

Nick put his hand on the small of her back and steered her easily through the crowded room, nodding pleasantly to people as they walked. 'No, not those, Amanda—the new pieces are in another room. I'd be happy to show them to you. That is,' he added teasingly, 'if you're not too busy.'

'You're not going to use that old line on me, are you?' she asked, smiling at him. 'You know, come up and see my etchings?'

'Is that another one of your American expressions?' he asked innocently, taking her hand in his. 'I'm not familiar with it.'

Amanda came to a sudden stop. 'I think you are,' she said, adding suspiciously, 'Where are these things you want to show me?'

'They're just through the door here, in my private

rooms. It will only take a few minutes.'

'I'm not moving another step,' she said firmly, but he ignored her and pulled her along with him. 'Nick,' she said, more loudly than she'd expected, 'I'm absolutely not going to your bedroom with you!'

A tall, distinguished-looking man standing near them turned around and laughed with delight. 'I'll bet that's the very first time you heard that one, Nicky! I'm glad to have been a witness to such a monumental event. Of course, the price of my silence, if you don't want this spread around, is an introduction to this charming young woman.'

Amanda blushed furiously, but Nick only grinned and extended his hand.

'Charles,' he said warmly, 'I'm delighted to see you. How are you? Amanda, this is Charles Harrow, an old friend and my personal physician. Charlie is also with our public health service. Charlie, this is Amanda Sutton.'

'I'm with Olsen & Tibbs,' Amanda added hastily. 'I'm here on business.'

Charles Harrow laughed again and took her hand in his. 'A business associate, hey? Well, my dear, you're the best-looking business associate Nicky's ever had. No wonder he wants to conduct his business in private!'

'Charlie, you're embarrassing the poor girl.' Amanda turned to the pretty, petite woman who had joined them. She smiled at Amanda. 'How do you do, Miss Sutton? I'm Shalal Harrow, Charlie's long-suffering wife.' She linked her arm through her husband's and he beamed affectionately at her. 'Charlie isn't very subtle. Isn't that right, Nicky?'

'Absolutely, Shalal. That's why I'm glad you're the paediatrician, not he. He'd scare off all his patients.'

'It's very nice to meet you,' Amanda said stiffly.

'Oh, no, my dear, the pleasure is all ours, believe me.

We'd heard all about Miss Amanda Sutton, and we couldn't wait to see you. Young women with engineering degrees are something different for our Nicky, aren't they, Shalal?'

Shalal sighed. 'You're impossible, Charlie! What must the poor girl think of us? Actually, we've heard some very nice things about you from Nick, Amanda. Why don't you go ahead and meet the others while I try and muzzle my terrible husband? I'm sure we'll see you later.'

Amanda managed a polite smile as she moved off with Nick, frantically wondering what he might have said about her to the Harrows. Nick looked down at her and sighed.

'What is it, Amanda?' he asked. 'Is it so awful to be seen with me? Would you feel more comfortable wearing a little tag that identified you as my business associate?'

'I just don't want people to assume anything, that's all,' she said tensely. 'Your friend Charlie. . .'

'My friend Charlie was just teasing you, Amanda, nothing more. And this isn't a business conference, you know, it's a celebration. Why don't you just relax a little and try to enjoy yourself?' Suddenly he put his arms around her. 'Don't struggle,' he said soothingly. 'We're in the middle of the dance-floor, in case you hadn't noticed. I'm sure you wouldn't want to draw attention to yourself again, now would you?' Grudgingly, Amanda stopped trying to free herself from his encircling arm. 'That's better,' he murmured approvingly, gathering her against him and moving slowly in rhythm to the music.

'People are watching us,' she whispered unhappily.

'People always look at beautiful women, Amanda. Well, as long as they are, let's give them something to watch, shall we?'

He gathered her more closely against him, and she

winced and closed her eyes as her glance met Charles Harrow's knowing smile. She held herself stiffly at first, trying without success to back away from Nick. Then, gradually, the soft music and the expert movement of his body began to relax her. She became aware of the long, muscled feel of his back under her fingers and the steady beat of his heart under her cheek. Even the smell of him was enticing, a subtle blend of lime and his own special masculine scent. She could feel his breath fanning her hair, and her eyelids drooped as she let her body lean into his. Nick seemed to sense what was happening to her, and he moved slightly so that his mouth was against her hair.

'Nicky!' a woman's voice shrilled, and Amanda pulled back from Nick's arms as if she had been awakened from a dream. A tall, stunning brunette, whose face and figure she recognised from dozens of magazine covers, flung her arms around Nick and kissed him. Amanda struggled to pull away from him, but he kept his arm firmly around her waist until finally the girl drew back and smiled at him poutingly.

'That's quite a greeting, Yasmin!' grinned Nick.

'I haven't see you in ages, Nicky,' she purred softly. 'Where have you been keeping yourself?'

'I've been doing a lot of travelling lately. And, of course, I've been wrapped up in a new business deal.'

'Of course you have,' she said, casting a meaningful glance at Amanda.

'As a matter of fact,' Nick said pleasantly, drawing Amanda more closely into his encircling arm, 'Miss Sutton is involved in it with me. Amanda, this is Yasmin DuPont, an old friend.'

The girl smiled slightly. 'You're part of Nicky's business deal? How fascinating!'

Nick chuckled softly. 'Miss Sutton is an engineer,

Yasmin,' he said, before Amanda could make any response.

'Really? Well, then, I can see why your new venture would require so much of your time.'

'I'm here with my employer, representing my company,' Amanda said in a tightly controlled voice, but Yasmin ignored her completely.

'I'll see you later, Nicky,' she whispered, touching his arm lightly. '*Au revoir.*'

Nick nodded and took Amanda back into his arms, but she remained stiff and aloof as they danced.

'An old friend, Nicky?' she asked with heavy sarcasm. 'Do all your old friends greet you that way?'

'Some of them do,' he replied evenly, trying unsuccessfully to hold her more closely. 'Why? Does it matter to you?'

'No, of course not,' she snapped. 'What matters is that your. . .your "friend" Jasmine. . .'

'Yasmin,' he said calmly. 'It has the same meaning, but. . .'

'Yasmin, then, OK?' Amanda said, her voice rising in irritation. 'The point is, your old friend seemed to think I'm one of your "old friends" too. Or was she just teasing me, like Charles Harrow?'

'You really are confused, aren't you, Amanda?' Nick asked pleasantly, whirling her around the floor. 'We haven't known each other long enough to be "old" anything, now have we?'

'Will you please stop playing these word games with me?' she demanded. 'Where are you taking me?' she added angrily as Nick suddenly led her off the parquet dance-floor.

'Where you can calm down, Amanda,' he answered, ignoring her protests and tugging her along after him. 'Stop struggling,' he added firmly. 'You're making a

spectacle of yourself.' Before she could more than
splutter angrily, he led her across the hall and into
another room. 'Now take a few deep breaths and get
hold of yourself,' he ordered, shutting the door behind
them. 'Then, if you're a good girl, I'll show you the
sculptures I told you about.'

'Please stop talking to me as if I were a child!' she said
crossly. He was lounging against the closed door, arms
crossed, an amused expression on his face, and she knew
it would be useless to try and get past him. 'I really don't
know why you're treating me this way,' she said, as
calmly as possible. 'I'd appreciate it if you'd step aside
and let me leave.'

Nick looked at her steadily. 'You look as if you're
ready to explode, and I doubt if my guests would enjoy
it. Of course, they might find it entertaining, but I do
owe them some courtesy, don't I?'

'For heaven's sake,' she stormed, her eyes flashing in
fury, 'your guests don't need protection from me! I'm the
one who's been embarrassed and insulted ever since I got
here. First your pal, Charlie, assumes you're trying to
seduce me, then your. . . your "old friend" Yasmin,' she
grated, almost spitting the word out, 'assumes you
already have. And now here I am in this room, alone with
you, even after I made it clear that I didn't want to come
in here, and you tell me to get hold of myself?'

'Amanda,' Nick said patiently, 'you take offence too
easily. Those comments were just meant as friendly
banter, nothing more.'

'Those comments were probably accurate assessments
of the way you deal with women. I told you, right from
the day I came to work in Morocco, that I'm not like
that.'

'You're being foolish, Amanda,' he said calmly. 'Those
people were only teasing you. I'm sorry if you felt insulted.'

'Teasing?' she repeated, her voice rising in angry disbelief. 'They were teasing me about being just another acquisition? Well, maybe this does sound foolish to you, but I don't want to be thought of as if I was something to be acquired, like these paintings!' She threw her arms wide and gestured to the canvases that hung on the walls of the room. For the first time she became aware of the subtly lit paintings and the smaller bronze and marble figures around her, and she gazed at them in sudden silence. 'Well,' she said at last, 'at least you were truthful about these. Those pieces are by the same artist who did the sculpture in the other room, aren't they? And that. . .is that a Degas?' she asked quietly, moving towards the figure of a ballet dancer, her anger forgotten in the shock of her delighted amazement. 'It is, isn't it? It's a real Degas!'

Nick smiled and walked over to join her. 'Yes, it is. Do you like it?'

'Like it?' she breathed, lightly running her hand over the delicate bronze head of the little dancer. 'Oh, Nick, she's magnificent!'

'I told you that you'd enjoy the things in this room, Amanda. Take a look around you.'

Slowly she began to move around the room, admiring the lovely paintings and hesitantly touching the small, perfect sculptures. Hanging alongside a Matisse and a Picasso were some small, beautifully detailed water-colours of the desert. The scenes were starkly simple, yet striking.

'These are wonderful, Nick. But I don't think I've ever seen anything like them before.'

'No, you wouldn't have,' he said. 'But I'm glad you like them. They're my mother's work; she's always been quite talented. Here,' he said, putting his arm around her and leading her to the far wall, 'this is hers too—a

watercolour of my family's château just outside Paris. Do
you like it?'

'It's lovely. Everything in this room is lovely. I must
admit, I never expected anything like it. It's like a
museum, isn't it? Like the Metropolitan in New York, or
a gallery on 57th Street, only there aren't any crowds, or
noisy schoolchildren, or. . .' Her words trailed off into
silence, and she shook her head. 'I don't know what to
say.'

'You don't need to say anything, Amanda,' Nick said
quietly. 'I'm happy that the things that I enjoy give you
pleasure.'

She was suddenly aware of the silence of the room, and
the light touch of his hand on her waist. 'I. . .I should go
back and find Tim,' she said quickly.

'Not just yet. First, I want to show you the loveliest
thing here.'

'There can't be any one thing in this room more
beautiful than another,' she said nervously as he led her
towards a shadowed corner.

'But there is, Amanda. Something unique. Something
I don't think you've ever really seen before.'

They stopped before a richly framed mirror, its silvery
surface smoky with age.

'The mirror is very handsome, I agree, but surely the
Degas is more beautiful,' she began in a puzzled tone,
then her eyes lifted and met his reflection in the mirror.
She drew in her breath. Nick was staring at her with
intimate intensity, his blue eyes boring into hers. The
sudden silence in the great room seemed to close in from
all sides, and she jumped as she watched the reflection of
his hand move towards her face.

'You're like a skittish colt,' he whispered, tilting her chin
up gently. 'There's nothing to be afraid of, Amanda. Look
at yourself, little one. You're the loveliest thing here.'

'Please,' she protested, trying to turn away, 'don't do this.'

'Look into the mirror, Amanda,' he persisted quietly, moving ever so slightly so he stood behind her. 'Tell me what you see.'

From the depths of the smoky mirror her reflection gazed back at her like the ghost of a stranger. She could see the rosy hue of her cheeks, the colour heightened by her embarrassment, and the startled look in her eyes, along with something else hidden in them, something caused by the touch of Nick's cool fingers. His hand slipped to her neck and she shivered.

'What do you see?' he demanded softly.

'I. . .I see myself, of course,' she said shakily.

'And?' he urged, his eyes catching hold of hers. 'Tell me who you see in the mirror.'

'This is ridiculous,' she whispered. She was painfully conscious of the press of Nick's lean, hard body against her back. Even as she watched, a tiny pulse began to beat rapidly in the hollow of her throat.

'Shall I tell you what I see?' he whispered softly. 'I see a lovely young woman who tries to hide her beauty from the world. I see lips set in determination that should smile more often. I see sensitive eyes that seem clouded with sadness.' His hand brushed her cheek and moved to the back of her neck. 'I want to kiss you, Amanda, and keep kissing you until I awaken the sleeping princess locked within you.'

'Nick,' she pleaded, in a voice so faint that she barely recognised it as her own, 'please stop.'

'I've never known a woman like you, little one,' he murmured, his fingers moving softly against the nape of her neck. 'You're everything a woman should be, and more.'

'You're wrong,' she said quickly. 'I'm not the woman

you're describing. I'm. . .I'm just me.'

'Yes, Amanda, you are, and you're unique. Each time we're together, I feel as if another layer of the woman you are is unfolding before me. I want to know all of that woman. I want to make love to her.'

He pulled the tortoiseshell pins from her hair, and the long golden tresses that she had so carefully pinned up earlier that evening fell languorously to her shoulders. He caught a handful of her hair in his fist and raised it to his mouth.

'Your hair is like a soft silken tent, Amanda. I'd like to feel it all around me.'

A tremor of anticipation ran through her and she watched, transfixed by his words, his touch, as he lowered his head until his mouth touched the back of her neck. His lips were warm and soft against her skin, gentle on the tender flesh behind her ear. His mouth moved slowly down her neck, tracing a searing pattern of soft kisses to her throat, and Amanda swayed against him. She felt as if she were falling into the mirror, as if the image of herself reflected there were calling out to her. Nick's arm tightened and he held her even more closely, until she could no longer be certain where his body began and hers ended.

'Please,' she moaned, but she no longer knew what she was pleading for.

'Watch the woman in the mirror, little one,' he whispered huskily.

Amanda sighed and stirred against him. His hand was on her shoulder, and she watched as if in a dream as he drew off the blue chiffon scarf and let it fall to the floor. She could see the tautness of her nipples through the clinging silk of her gown, and she watched while Nick's hands travelled slowly to her breasts, until he gently cupped them in their silken housing. Again her eyes met his in the shadowy mirror. They were darkened and flickering with passion, and they were fixed on the reflection of her face. Only his hands seemed to know her body, and wherever they touched, they ignited her skin to flame. Suddenly he twisted his strong fingers into her thick hair and turned her towards him. She was lost in the smell and touch of him, and as his head lowered towards her she tried to escape what was happening to her.

'Nick, don't,' she whispered, 'please don't,' but even to her own ears her words were faint and without meaning. Her hands moved up tentatively to touch his face, to bring his mouth to hers.

'Let yourself go, Amanda,' he said. 'Don't be afraid. That is how it's meant to be between men and women.'

It was as though cold water had been thrown on her, and with a sudden awakening she pulled free of his arms.

'Is that what this is all about?' she demanded. 'A seduction scene, to prove a point?'

'What are you talking about, Amanda?' he asked, reaching out for her again.

'I'm talking about this. . .this little charade of yours!' she snapped, moving away from him. 'I'm talking about this sorry attempt to reduce me to the only kind of woman you understand.'

'You're not making sense,' he said harshly. 'This is no charade, Amanda.'

'Then it's an object lesson. You said I needed a man to set me free, didn't you? I suppose the point of all this is to prove that you were right, and that you're that man.' She smiled coldly. 'You almost had me fooled for a while, do you know that? All that talk, that charm, that was just to. . .to lull me into the right kind of mood, wasn't it? And this room. . .it's the perfect setting for the scene we were supposed to play, isn't it? The only way you can deal with a woman is by feeding your own ego, by making her into some kind of. . .of object, something you can add to your collection. I suppose I should feel flattered, shouldn't I? You must have spent days orchestrating this. Or have you used this same setting before?'

'Damn it, Amanda,' Nick snapped angrily, grabbing her arm, 'stop talking as if this were a play! There's no audience to applaud at the final curtain—there's only a man and a woman opening themselves to each other, giving and taking, becoming more together than they were separately.'

'That's a pretty speech,' she said bitterly, 'but we both know who does the giving, and who does the taking, don't we? Women give, and men take.'

Nick stared at her, the anger gone from his face. 'Whoever taught you about love made a poor job of it,' he said slowly.

'You're wrong, Nick,' she said calmly. 'I've been taught by experts. And I learned my lessons well, I assure you.'

'I don't think so,' he said. 'You can't really believe that. And if you do, it's time you learned the truth.'

Before she could move away he drew her into his arms again.

'You don't know when to give up, do you?' she asked coldly. 'What happens next? Are you going to take me forcibly? That's a little out of character even for you, don't you think?'

His arms tightened around her and his hands moved slowly across her back. 'I'm going to try to warm what's left of your soul, Amanda,' he whispered. 'I'm going to remind you of what you almost let yourself be just a few moments ago.'

She started to answer, but he bent his head and covered her mouth with his. She struggled furiously, but his mouth was insistent, demanding at first, then gentling upon hers. She felt as if she was melting in the warmth of his kiss, as if she was being drawn into a whirlpool, and her anger, her resolution, began to slip away in the rush of sensation. Nothing mattered but this moment, this feeling. Her lips softened under his, and her mouth parted of its own volition. With a soft moan, part need, part despair she moved her hands up to embrace him, to touch the thick hair at the nape of his neck. Nick shuddered and whispered her name against her mouth, and she pressed herself against him, no longer aware of anything but the feel and taste of him. Nick's hands moved to her shoulders, touching, touching, flaming her skin everywhere. She sighed as his fingers slipped the straps from the bodice of her gown, suffused with a trembling weakness, and she felt herself opening to him, melting under his caresses. His mouth left hers and touched the velvet skin about her breast.

As if in a dream, she became aware of a pounding at the door. Bewildered, she pulled free of Nick's arms, and only then did they both realise that the room had been plunged into darkness.

'What the devil. . . ?' Nick swore, striding to the door and yanking it open. 'Yes, what is it? What's going on out there?'

The butler stood in the darkened corridor, his face illuminated by the lit candle he carried.

'I'm sorry to disturb you, sir, but there's been an overload at the power station, and this part of the city has no light. Some of your guests are a bit distressed, and I thought you might wish to reassure them. However, if you prefer not to be disturbed, sir. . .' His sweeping glance passed quickly over Amanda, and she blushed.

Nick hesitated only briefly. 'No, you did the right thing. I'll attend to it,' he turned to Amanda. 'I'm sorry,' he said softly, but she was already clutching her chiffon scarf tightly around her shoulders.

'Not at all,' she said, hoping the coolness of her voice was sufficient to disguise the trembling of her body. 'I was just leaving anyway.'

'Amanda. . .'

'I'm sorry, Your Excellency,' she said, not daring to meet his eyes. 'We've more than finished.'

Nick stood still as she strode quickly past him to the door and the safety of the servant in the hallway. 'Saved by the bell,' he said quietly. 'Isn't that one of your American expressions?'

'Goodnight,' said Amanda, moving swiftly down the corridor. There was no answer, but she could feel Nick's eyes burning through her back all the way to the door.

CHAPTER FIVE

THE NEXT morning, sounds of traffic drifting up from the
street below awoke Amanda from a disturbed, dream-
racked sleep. Exhausted from her restless night, her head
throbbing, she lay in bed trying to make some sense out
of the confused images that had plagued her through the
night.

Her dreams had been of her former husband, Todd,
recalling with brutal clarity fragments and scenes from
the brief, unhappy marriage she had rushed into when
she was only eighteen. He had been a senior and she a
freshman, although she had left university after their
elopement to support them both. For the first few
months she had been happy and contented; then he had
started staying out late at night. She had believed him
when he told her he had late night research to do at the
university library, patiently sitting at home alone,
waiting for him, trusting in him, loving him, until finally
the mushrooming rumours on campus forced her to face
the truth. The stark reality of the final scene of their life
together rushed back to her, just as it had during the
dream-filled night.

Todd had come home just past midnight, tiptoeing
into their tiny living room, surprised to find her waiting
for him in the dark.

'It's time you stopped lying to me, Todd,' she said
wearily, her voice hoarse with unshed tears. 'You weren't
at the library, tonight or any other night. I know all
about the other women; everybody knows, I guess. How
could you do this to me? I thought you loved me.'

75

He hung his jacket in the closet with elaborate care and turned to her. 'I do, Mandy,' he said innocently. 'But there's a whole world out there, just waiting for me. Try and understand.'

'I can't,' she groaned brushing the tears from her cheeks with the palms of her hands. 'Isn't someone who loves you all the world you need?'

'You're my wife,' he said with the boyish grin she knew so well. 'I'll always come home to you.'

She shook her head in despair. 'That's not a marriage,' she whispered.

'Well, it is for me,' he said flatly. 'Get used to it.'

It was then that she had slapped his face hard, with all the pent-up fury and pain exploding within her. And, for the first time, she went to her mother and told her everything.

'I tried to warn you, Amanda,' her mother had said, turning away from her daughter's tear-stained face. 'But you just wouldn't learn from my mistake, would you? Men are all the same, child. They take and take, and when they're finished they walk off and leave you. Your father proved that to us both when he walked out.'

'But I loved Todd, Mother,' she sobbed.

Her mother laughed harshly. 'And I loved your father,' she said bitterly. 'That just makes it easier for them to hurt us, don't you see?' She grabbed her daughter's shoulders with a sudden ferocity and shook her. 'Just remember what you've learned, child. Depend on yourself, and you won't ever need anybody selse. That's the way to survive.'

And survive she had, she thought, downing two aspirins to ease the throbbing in her head. Wrapping her robe around herself, Amanda stared into the bathroom mirror. There'd been no mistakes, no errors—until last night. Her reflected image seemed to dissolve, to be replaced by what she had seen as she had gazed into the mirror in Nick's room. She thought of the way she had felt watching him touch her, the way she had felt when he kissed her, and she shook her head in disbelief. Picking up her brush, she attacked her long hair with hard, angry strokes. She was her own worst enemy, she thought angrily, letting her emotions carry her away and deceive her, when the truth was that Nick was like all the rest, a man who climbed mountains simply because they existed. A woman was a challenge, especially one he couldn't have.

She put down the hairbrush and stared at herself, satisfied with what she saw. The woman in the mirror last night had been a mirage, something conjured up in a moment of weakness.

By nine o'clock, when she reached her office, Amanda felt in control of her life again. She went through her mail, setting aside those things that had to be dealt with immediately. She buzzed Helen and asked her to bring in her messages.

'How was the party last night?' Helen asked eagerly, her face aglow with curiosity. 'I'll bet the Sheikh's place is really something! And what about him? I mean, I know he's gorgeous, but what's he really like?'

'How am I supposed to know?' Amanda snapped irritably. 'I'm sorry, Helen,' she added quickly, 'I didn't mean to jump on you like that—I guess the heat is getting to me today. You're right; his home is like something out of the Arabian Nights.'

'And? What about the guy himself? You must have spent some time alone with him. Is he as charming as everybody says?'

'He's a self-centred, egotistical. . .' Amanda bit her lip and broke off in mid-sentence. 'Look,' she said, busily shuffling the papers on her desk, 'isn't there any work that needs doing around here? What's with all these questions?'

'Nothing much,' her secretary answered casually, except that self-centred, egotistical guy's been calling you all morning.'

'All morning? It's only just past nine. When did his office start phoning?'

'Not his office, A.S.,' Helen giggled, 'the man himself. He's been calling since about eight, and the last time he sounded pretty annoyed. He said to tell you you were to call him at once, before you did anything else.'

'Did he really?' muttered Amanda, arching her eyebrows. 'Well, I have other things to do first.' Turning away from the perplexed expression on Helen's face, she began to burrow in her briefcase. 'If he calls again, just tell him I'll get back to him as soon as possible.'

As the door to her office closed, Amanda sank back in her chair with a sigh. She'd been a fool the night before, she thought glumly, and Nick was not about to let her forget it. Blindly she began to sort through her mail again, scribbling notes on a memo pad and trying to concentrate on business. Just as she had begun to organise her day, she was startled by the sound of the door slamming, and she looked up in surprise and found Tim Pauling standing before her, a look of irritation on his face.

'I'm sorry to disturb you, Sutton,' he said, a bite of sarcasm in his tone, 'but we seem to have a bit of a problem.'

'What's the matter, Tim? Is anything wrong at the site?'

Tim pushed some papers aside and perched on the corner of her desk, sighing deeply as he did. 'No, no, it's nothing like that. Look, kid, I want you to level with me. Are you having some kind of problem with this account?'

Carefully Amanda capped her pen and folded her hands on her desk. 'No,' she said slowly, 'not that I know of. Why? Has the Sheikh—has there been a complaint about me?'

Tim waved his hand and shook his head. 'Oh, no, Amanda, nothing like that. Matter of fact, Nick told me the other day that you're doing a great job, far as he's concerned. It's just that—well, take this morning, for instance. I just got a call from him. He said he's been trying to reach you for the past couple of hours in order to check out some figures, but you aren't accepting his calls.'

'I never said that, Tim. I only got in a while ago, and I have a lot to do. I thought I'd phone him after I'd gone through some of these reports.'

Tim sighed again. 'Look, kid,' he said patiently, 'the reports can wait: Nicholas ben Saad can't. It's as simple as that. I know you're new to this game, but the client always comes first, understand? Now, if you can't handle it. . .'

His words trailed off into silence, but their meaning was clear. Amanda reached for the phone, knowing that Tim wouldn't tolerate any more excuses. He waited while she dialled Nick's number, then gave her a mock salute and left. To her surprise, Nick answered the telephone himself.

'I'm sorry I wasn't available when you called earlier, Nick, but I hadn't expected you would begin your day so early.'

'Why not, Amanda? Did you think I'd have difficulty sleeping after what happened last night?'

'Nothing happened,' she responded quickly, glad he couldn't see the colour rise in her cheeks.

He laughed softly. 'We must have been at two different parties, Amanda. Of course something happened. How could you have put it out of your mind so easily?'

'It was a mistake,' she said haltingly. 'And I guess it was as much my fault as yours. Can't we just forget the whole thing?'

'I don't understand, Amanda,' he said, and she could hear the carefully concealed laughter in his voice. 'I was referring to the power failure. Surely you're not responsible for that?'

She bit her lip and closed her eyes, determined not to be drawn into this game. 'I'm very rushed this morning, Nick. I haven't got any time to spare.'

'What is it you're so busy with, Amanda?' he asked pleasantly.

'I'm going through progress reports from the site.'

'I'm glad to hear that,' he answered. 'For a while this morning I wondered if you'd forgotten that you're working for me. I think that entitles me to some of your time, doesn't it?'

'Yes, certainly it does,' she said stiffly. 'I'm sorry I was abrupt. How may I help you?'

'That's much better,' he said soothingly. 'Actually, I called about the current cost figures. If you have an update on them, I'd like to see them.'

'Certainly. I should have them ready by late afternoon. I'll send someone over with them by three or four o'clock.'

'No, don't do that, Amanda—I'm going to be tied up elsewhere at a meeting by then. Why don't you bring them with you this evening? We can go through them together after dinner.'

She almost laughed aloud. The trap he'd set for her was so obvious it was a joke. 'That's impossible, Nick,' she said, pleased with how easily the lie came to her. 'I've made dinner plans with someone here at the office.'

There was only a brief pause. 'I see. Well, I thought you'd prefer to go over the material tonight since Tim is joining me for dinner, but if you can't manage that my chauffeur can pick you up at your hotel when he drops Tim off. Shall we make it eleven o'clock?'

Amanda winced and put her hand to her head. Score one for Nicholas ben Saad, she thought. 'No, don't do that—I'll cancel my dinner plans. I'll be ready whenever Tim is.'

'I thought you might be,' laughed Nick. 'I'll see you tonight.'

The long business day passed in a whirlwind of activity. Amanda cancelled a luncheon appointment with Tim, pleading overwork. When he commented on her efficiency and dedication, she forced herself to smile. Actually, she was working feverishly to compile all the facts and figures Nick might need so there would be no possible reason to meet with him again, at least not in the near future.

As the sun set, streaks of amber and red lingered in the cloudless blue sky like feather strokes on an artist's palette. The late afternoon heat was a palpable presence on Amanda's skin as she slipped into a cool, pale yellow dress, its curved neckline accentuated by a wide, shirred waistband and softly flared skirt. Standing before her mirror, she brushed her long blonde hair until it gleamed with refracted light. It fell softly about her face and shoulders, compensating for the fact that she wore no necklace or earrings.

'Just remember, Amanda Sutton,' she told her reflection, 'you're all business!'

The dusk-cooled shadows fell as Nick's limousine made the long, winding approach to his town house through a stand of stately cypresses. A housekeeper greeted them at the massive front door and then led them to a small, intimate dining-room somewhat distant from the grand salon they had been in the night before. There were cool terracotta tiles on the floor, unrelieved except for the occasional flash of colour lent by small, exquisite Rya rugs. The walls were hung with magnificent Persian miniatures, alive with vivid colour and etched in gold. Alternating with them were lovely watercolours and charcoal sketches of Parisian street scenes.

'I see you've discovered the two sides of me,' said Nick, coming into the room towards them. 'My French mother and my Bedouin father seem to claim equal parts of my soul.'

Amanda's breath caught painfully at the sight of him. Informally dressed in a blue shirt, tan cashmere jacket, and navy trousers, he was even more attractive than the night before. His thick black hair looked somewhat damp, as if he'd just showered, and she remembered the sensual feel of it beneath her fingers. Although she feared that the hammering of her heart could be heard throughout the room, her voice was cool and impersonal as she extended her hand to Nick.

'Good evening,' she said politely. 'This is a lovely room.'

'Yes, I think so,' he answered, raising her hand to his mouth. His every action, every word was correct and proper, but the intensity emanating from him and the touch of his mouth on her hand made her pulse race. 'You look particularly beautiful tonight, Amanda.'

Flushed and confused by her own emotions, she lowered her eyes and turned towards Tim, who seemed completely unaware of the electric current in the air.

'Isn't she terrific? Bright as well as beautiful. It's a pleasure to see you, Nick. This is certainly a better setting for a working dinner than I'm used to.'

'I try to combine business with pleasure if it's at all

possible. That's one of the reasons I'm looking forward to our trip to the construction site, Tim. The desert is exceptionally beautiful this time of year. You'll enjoy it, I'm sure, and of course you'll get a first-hand view of some of the problems we've been running into.'

'I wanted to talk to you about that, Nick,' Tim said quickly. 'Unfortunately, I'm going to have to beg off. I got a call from Les Grant in the New York office. He's run into some serious problems on the materials end, and I'll have to fly back and deal with them if we want to keep things moving on schedule.'

Amanda turned a shocked face to her boss. 'When did this happen?' she demanded. 'And why didn't you tell me?'

Tim frowned a warning at her. 'I never got the chance, Sutton—you cancelled our lunch date, remember? Anyway, it's no problem. You'll just have to take over on your own a little sooner than we'd expected. That is, if it's OK with you, Nick.'

Nick had been listening to their discussion with interest, and now he smiled reassuringly at them both. 'Of course, Tim. I have every confidence in Amanda. Isn't that right?' he asked her, and somehow she managed a convincing response.

The tension of the moment passed, and they sat down to dinner. Amanda's confidence grew as the evening wore on. Throughout the informal meal, Nick was attentive but impersonal, dividing his attention equally between her and Tim. Finally, after espresso, cheese and fruit had been served, Tim pushed back from the table and reached into his pocket.

'Nick, I have the figures you requested.' He glanced at his watch. 'I hate to hurry things, but we're going to have to review them now if I'm going to get any sleep at all. I'm booked on the morning flight—it was all I could get on such short notice.'

'Sorry, Tim,' Nick said pleasantly, 'but I forgot some papers I need. Gamal will be along with them, but he's not going to be able to join us until later.' He turned to Amanda and smiled. 'Since Amanda is the one who's going to be handling things from now on, why don't you go back to the hotel and let her wait here for Gamal?'

'No!' She spoke so quickly and shrilly that Tim stared at her in surprise. 'I mean, suppose something needs your approval, Tim?'

'Don't be silly, Sutton. These are just cost runs, nothing to approve or disapprove. Besides, I'm turning the whole show over to you as of tomorrow, remember? Don't bother seeing me out, Nick, I can find the way.'

There was nothing more to say. Amanda sat quietly while the housekeeper cleared the table, then she began to sort through the papers Tim had given her, uncomfortably aware of Nick's silent scrutiny.

'I think we should get started, Nick,' she at last said. 'There are lots of figures to go through.'

Nick smiled and leaned back in his chair. 'There's no point in doing that until Gamal gets here,' he said. 'And I haven't finished my second cup of coffee yet, anyway. Are you sure you don't want some?'

'No,' she said quickly, 'no, thank you. Actually, I'd like to finish up and get back to the hotel. It's been a long day.'

He sipped at his coffee and looked thoughtfully at her. 'Don't you think we ought to talk about what happened last night?' he said suddenly. 'Or am I just supposed to keep on pretending it didn't happen?'

'There's nothing to talk about,' she said stiffly, looking away from him.

'I don't agree, Amanda.'

'It doesn't matter whether you agree or not,' she

answered quickly. 'I told you this morning, I'm as much to blame as you are, and I simply want to forget the whole thing. If you can't accept that. . .'

'Yes?' he asked softly. 'What then, Amanda?'

She pushed her chair back from the table and rose to her feet. 'Then I'm going to leave, Nick. You have the figures you need; I'm sure you can understand them without my help. After Gamal gets here, if you have any questions, you can phone me at my hotel.'

He stood up and smiled at her. 'I see. Tim is leaving tomorrow, turning the responsibility for this project over to you, and your very first official act is to walk out without doing your job. That's not very encouraging, Amanda.'

She drew in her breath and turned to face him. 'That's not what I'm doing and you know it,' she said.

'That's how it looks to me,' he said politely. 'I'm sure that's how Tim would see it, too.'

She stared at him for a moment, then shrugged her shoulders in resignation. 'Have it your way. I'll stay, if you insist. I'll just stand here until Gamal arrives.'

She turned away and walked across the room, to the French doors leading out to the flagstone terrace. Nick hadn't moved, but she could sense his eyes boring into her, and finally she stepped through the open doors, trying to put as much distance between them as she could. She tilted her head back and stared at the blackness of the night sky. A crescent moon rode high above, its pale glow a milky contrast to the bright stars that seemed to pierce the darkness. A cool night breeze, scented with the perfume of flowers in the garden, played across her skin, and she shivered.

'Are you cool?' asked Nick, and she turned in surprise. 'Would you like my jacket?'

'No, no, I'm fine, thank you. I. . .I just wanted a

breath of air.' He was standing so close to her that she could almost reach out and touch him, and in sudden confusion she moved towards the reflecting pool in the centre of the terrace. Shimmering streams of water cascaded from a fountain in its midst, and hidden lights turned each drop of water into a multi-faceted jewel.

'It's a beautiful night, isn't it?' he said softly, walking to her side.

'Yes,' she said quickly, 'but you were right, it is cool. I think I'll go back inside. Then, when Gamal gets here. . .'

'Why are you afraid of me?' he asked suddenly, with a directness that startled her.

'I'm not,' she said, looking away from him.

'Then why do you run away from me each time I get too close, Amanda? You're like a kit fox, in the desert, afraid of being caught.'

'I don't know what you're talking about,' she insisted. 'I came here to do a job, and I'm just trying to do it the best way I can.'

Nick put his hands on her shoulders and turned her to face him. 'But you found more here than a job, didn't you?' he asked. 'And that's what you're afraid to admit, even to yourself.'

An electric current seemed to pass from his fingers to her skin, and she shook her head in denial of what she felt as much as in denial of his words.

'Why won't you leave me alone?' she whispered. 'It isn't fair to do this to me, Nick.'

'It isn't fair to lie to yourself, Amanda,' he said softly, tilting her chin upwards until her eyes met his. 'I know that you feel what I feel, want what I want. Why won't you admit it?'

'You're wrong,' she insisted desperately, suddenly afraid he could see into her very soul. 'Please believe me.'

A cloud passed over the moon, and his face was lost in shadow. His eyes, reflecting the lights from the fountain, seemed to swallow her whole. Gently he cupped her face in his hands.

'I do believe you, little one. I believe what I see in your eyes. The eyes are the window to the soul, Amanda, did you know that? And yours are telling me everything I need to know.'

He bent his head towards her, blotting out the night sky. Gently, almost delicately, his mouth touched hers. She stood perfectly still, not daring to move, afraid to face what was happening to all her carefully made promises, all her steely determination, all her senses concentrated on the feel of Nick's lips on hers. His fingers spread, moving into the silken softness of her hair, and she rose on tiptoe, striving upwards to him, her mouth moving softly under his, but still she held her body taut. His hands were on the back of her head now, buried in her hair, and his kiss was changing, becoming more demanding and urgent. Slowly, her lips parted under his, and as if from a great distance, she heard herself whimper as the honeyed taste of him filled her mouth, and suddenly her hands moved up to touch his chest, feeling the hard planes of muscle under her fingers. Her arms wound around his neck as he whispered her name. His strong hands were moving down her back, pulling her so tightly against him that she could feel the hardness of him along every inch of her body. He bent her back in his arms, exposing the long, smooth column of her throat. His lips were warm against her flesh, burning the hollows of her neck with their touch, caressing the night chill away from her.

'Nick,' she whispered, 'Gamal isn't coming, is he?'

'No,' he murmured against her compliant mouth. 'Are you sorry?'

Her answer was lost as his mouth possessed hers with a questing urgency that set them both on fire. He kissed her until her lips felt swollen and bruised with passion, but even then she couldn't satisfy her need for the taste and feel of him, and she grasped the nape of his neck and ground her mouth against his. He caught her lower lip in his teeth and bit it gently, and she moaned with passion. There was a pounding in her ears; even her blood felt thick with desire as her body seemed to strain and swell towards his mouth and hands. He wrapped her golden hair in one powerful hand as the other moved slowly over her. Gently his fingers moved up and cupped her breast, and she gasped as his hand caressed the full, soft curve. Even through the soft fabric of her clothing, she could feel his touch on her nipple, and it hardened and pressed into his palm. He lowered his head and kissed the straining fabric covering her breast, and she sighed with pleasure, trying to fit all her yielding flesh to his. His hand moved down her soft body, brushing her thighs, then he cupped her buttocks and drew her tightly against him.

'Nick, please,' she whispered, but it was a protest without meaning.

'You're so lovely, Amanda.' His voice was hoarse with passion as he found her mouth again. 'I want to see all of you, to worship your body with my mouth, my hands, with every part of me.'

Lost in his arms, lost in something greater than desire, lost to herself, she barely heard the sibilant hiss of her zipper and the faint rustle of her dress as it fell in a soft heap at her feet. The moon cast its cold white glow over them as they strained towards each other, and Nick whispered her name as he swept her into his strong arms. Quickly he crossed the terrace and lowered her gently on to a silk-covered chaise-longue that stood beneath the tall trees.

'Be mine, little one,' he said softly as he lowered himself beside her.

Nothing mattered but his touch, his kisses, and she surrendered herself to his mouth. Gently he pulled down the straps of her lace camisole.

'You're beautiful, Amanda,' he whispered, cupping her breasts in his hands. His fingers touched their swollen tips and she moaned in anticipation. Slowly his tongue traced the soft skin around the rosy tips until she felt as if each nerve in her body were on fire. At last his mouth closed gently around her breast and her hands pressed his head closer to her as her body began to move beneath his. Suddenly he pulled free of her arms, and she reached out for him, but he was ripping off his jacket and shirt and then he was against her again. Amanda stroked his naked skin, and his back felt as she had known it would, like smooth silk laid over rippling steel, and the touch of his chest against her naked breasts made her gasp aloud.

Never in her life had she felt like this. She wanted all of him, she wanted to be part of everything he was, to melt into him until there was no beginning and no end to her own self. She felt as if she were slipping away to an uncharted land, a place she had never been before, and a faint tingle of fear began to intrude upon her.

'Nick,' she whispered, a dim warning sounding over the pulse of blood in her ears, 'please, no more!'

His only response was to kiss her even more passionately. 'I want you so badly, Amanda,' he murmured as his hands touched her hips. His fingers closed on her lace panties and his mouth returned to hers again.

'Nick,' she begged, turning her head away, her voice sharper now, 'don't!'

His mouth stilled her words as his hands traced circles of desire on her skin, and she began to drift free of herself, succumbing to the torrent of emotions washing over her. And then, with a last desperate effort, as if she were drowning, flailing about in the treacherous water in a final attempt to find help before sinking into a feeling of welcome acquiescence, she thought of what it would really mean to give herself to him. Suddenly she admitted the terrifying truth to herself: her body would be the least important thing she would surrender to this man. Once Nick possessed her, he would control her mind and soul as well. With a harsh, frightened cry, she pushed him from her.

'No!' she gasped, wrapping her arms around herself in instinctive protection. 'I don't want this!'

He knelt beside her and turned her face towards him. 'Look at me, Amanda,' he said quietly. 'Look at me and tell me you don't want me.' Slowly she raised her head, but her eyes couldn't meet his. 'You can't say it, can you?'

She took a deep breath and forced herself to look directly at him. 'I don't want to do this,' she said quickly. 'It was a mistake.' Nick reached out to her, but she brushed his hand aside. 'It was a mistake,' she repeated evenly, pulling up the straps of her camisole, 'and it's gone too far.'

He leaned back and studied her face. 'It wasn't a mistake, Amanda, you know that. It was *kismet*— something predestined, preordained—something it's useless to deny. What we feel for each other is *kismet*.'

With a panic born of desperation, Amanda realised she had to hurt him in order to escape what was happening to her, had to remove him from her life if she were to restructure her fragmenting perspective.

'That's very poetic,' she answered, the calmness of her voice giving no hint of what she felt, 'but the simple fact is that I never intended the game to go this far.'

She slid past him as a wispy cloud trailed across the moon, snatching up her yellow dress from the terrace, while Nick stared at her in confusion.

'You're not making any sense, Amanda. This isn't a game.'

'But it is, Your Excellency,' she said, her fingers trembling as she smoothed her dress down the length of her body. 'This time, I decided we'd play by my rules.'

'Games? Rules?' he said slowly. 'What the hell are you talking about?'

'Just what I said,' she repeated. 'In your. . .your private little gallery last night, we played by your rules, and you—you did what you do very well.'

Nick ran his hand through his hair and got to his feet. 'I still don't know what you're talking about, Amanda. You keep trying to make me fit some stereotype, instead of admitting your feelings to yourself.'

She smoothed back her hair and slid her hands into the pockets of her dress. 'I don't blame you for being so defensive,' she said, in tones so cold they amazed her. 'After all, I've probably ruined your record. Just think, Your Excellency—in years to come, whenever I hear your name, I'll be able to remember that I was the first woman you couldn't have.'

He closed the remaining distance between them and stood looking at her in silence for a few seconds. 'Don't do this,' he said softly. 'Words are hard to forget, Amanda.

'So are actions,' she answered quickly, 'especially humbling ones. That's why I know you'll never forget me, either.'

His fingers closed around her wrist like steel manacles. 'Are you trying to tell me you planned all this?' he asked carefully.

'I'm good at what I do, too,' she said, forcing her eyes

to meet his. 'I think I told you that when we first met.'

'What are you saying?' he demanded. 'That this was a script you wrote? A play?' He shook his head and his eyes narrowed. 'I don't believe it, Amanda.' His flaring nostrils and hooded eyes gave his shadowed features a predatory look, but there was a hint of anguish in his voice, and she hesitated. Immediately, as if he sensed some weakness in her, Nick moved closer. 'It's not too late,' he said. 'Tell me what you've said isn't true, that what you felt in my arms was real. You couldn't have been pretending all that—no woman could.'

Bitter anger swept aside her final reservations. 'You mean no woman can resist you, don't you, Your Excellency? What more must I do to convince you? You wouldn't listen to me—I thought you were at least intelligent enough to accept defeat when it was presented to you in such simple, basic terms that even your monumental ego would understand it.'

'You mean it, don't you?' he growled. 'This was a. . .a performance, a play in which a woman forces a passionate man to his knees so she can humiliate him by telling him it was all an artfully constructed trap.'

'Very perceptive, Your Excellency,' she said. 'Painful, I suppose, but perceptive.'

Nick's grip on her wrist tightened painfully, then he released her and stepped back. 'You'd better leave, Miss Sutton,' he said, his voice cold and empty of emotion, 'otherwise I won't be responsible for my actions.'

'You don't have to threaten me,' Amanda answered quickly, a sharp thrill of fear running through her. 'I had planned to.'

He bared his teeth in a smile. 'I'm glad to hear it. It's occurred to me that I could play your script all the way to the end. After all, the next logical step would be for me to force you to the ground and do something we'd both regret—then at least you might show some honest emotion, one way or the other.'

'You wouldn't do that,' she said, backing away from him.

'No,' he admitted, 'I wouldn't. I feel too sorry for you to do that, Amanda.'

'You're wasting your pity,' she lashed back, anger overcoming her fear. 'Save it for yourself and your. . .your over-active libido!'

Nick looked at her in silence, then he shrugged his shoulders and turned away. 'This is pointless,' he said. 'We really have nothing more to say to each other, have we? I'll see to it that all further business between your office and mine is handled by Gamal. I'll have my chauffeur drive you back to your hotel.'

'I'd rather call a cab,' Amanda answered coldly.

Nick shrugged. 'As you wish, Miss Sutton. There's a phone just inside the house.'

He turned and walked silently into the darkness of the garden, and Amanda fled.

CHAPTER SIX

'WELL, Amanda,' said Helen as she brought in a stack of letters for Amanda's signature and dumped them on her desk, 'Tim's been gone a week and the office has survived. Don't you think it's time you eased off the work load a bit?'

Amanda began to leaf through the typed pages, scrawling her name at the bottom of each one. 'We've been over this before,' she said patiently. 'I know you think I've been working too hard, and I appreciate your concern, but I'm fine, really. Stop worrying about me.'

Helen looked at her boss, noting the dark circles under her eyes and the pallor of her skin. 'You don't have to spend twelve hours a day in this place, you know. I just don't understand why you don't take some time off.'

'Because I can't,' Amanda answered rather curtly. 'I didn't mean to snap at you,' she added quickly. 'Thanks for being so concerned, but, believe me, I know what I'm doing.'

'Well, I hope so,' said Helen in a tone that clearly suggested she thought otherwise. 'No job is worth working yourself ragged. I know, I know, you want me to stop mothering you. OK, I'll get back to work and leave you alone.'

Amanda eased her chair back from the desk and slumped wearily as her secretary left the room. She smiled ruefully as she thought of Helen's words. She might call her advice 'mothering', but it was as far removed from the way her own mother would have treated her as Morocco was from her home town in

California. Closing her eyes, she recalled the time the year before when she had had to call her mother and cancel a planned vacation trip home.

'I really looked forward to seeing you, Mother,' she had said, 'but my boss dumped a last-minute report on me today. We're short-handed in the office just now, and they asked me to reschedule my vacation.'

Her mother's cool, reserved voice had sounded as neutral as if she were waiting on a customer in her little dress shop on Fulton Street. 'Never apologise for working hard, Amanda,' she said. 'Anyway, the summer's almost over, and you know how busy it gets here in the fall. And then the Christmas rush starts and I always have more business than I can handle. Why don't we make it some time in the spring?'

There was a strange tightness in Amanda's throat when she answered. 'But I really wanted to see you, Mother. We haven't seen each other since I moved to New York.'

'I know, Amanda, but other obligations must come first, mustn't they, child?'

Amanda blinked back a sudden trickle of tears. 'Yes, of course,' she agreed softly. 'But I thought—well, one of the staff people offered to cover for me for a week next month. He said he'd. . .'

'I certainly wouldn't want to think you'd begun to rely on other people's favours, Amanda,' her mother chided. 'Particularly on the favours of a man you work with. Independence, child, remember? And self-reliance, Amanda. I thought you'd learned how important those things were. No, dear, you do your job and I'll do mine.' Her voice gentled and Amanda could almost picture her face softening into a smile. 'Just keep sending me those little memos from your company newsletter, dear. You'll never know what pleasure I get out of seeing your name mentioned every now and then.'

But she did know, Amanda thought grimly, as she pulled her chair back to her desk. Her mother's fury at her elopement with Todd had only been matched by the disdain with which she had greeted the news that Amanda was giving up her college scholarship to go to work and support her new husband.

'You fool!' she had snapped, the colour draining from her cheeks as she faced her love-struck eighteen-year-old daughter. 'I thought you'd learned something from me. You need a career, Amanda, a purpose. Now you'll have neither.'

'I can have a career some day, Mother,' she had insisted, still warmed by the glow of her weekend honeymoon. 'But I need Todd, too. I love him.'

'Love?' her mother said harshly. 'Love is a cheap emotion, Amanda. It's just another word for what men want from us.'

'Todd isn't like that, Mother,' she answered, thinking of the warmth he had brought into her empty life.

'They're all like that,' her mother answered quickly. 'You'll see. Men just can't be faithful, Amanda. I ought to know—just look at how your father ruined my life! They're all takers, every last one of them.'

It was advice she had learned to respect eventually, after the break up with Todd, after some of the men she worked with made it clear a woman had no place in engineering, after some of them even assumed she would sleep her way to the top. And she had never been vulnerable again, until now. With a sigh, she slammed shut her desk drawer. The long hours at the office had been the only way to get through the past week. Memories of the night in the garden with Nick kept intruding upon her unexpectedly, like flashes from an old movie. Her initial anger and humiliation had rapidly

TAKE FOUR
BEST SELLER ROMANCES
FREE!

♥

Best Sellers are for the true romantic! These stories are our favourite Romance titles re-published by popular demand.

♥

And to introduce to you this superb series, we'll send you four Best Sellers absolutely FREE when you complete and return this card.

♥

We're so confident that you will enjoy Best Sellers that we'll also reserve a subscription for you to the Mills & Boon Reader Service, which means you could enjoy...

♥

Four new novels sent direct to you every two months (before they're available in the shops).

Free postage and packing we pay all the extras.

Free regular Newsletter packed with special offers, competitions, author news and much, much more.

Mills & Boon — FREE BOOKS CERTIFICATE

YES! Please send me my four **FREE** Best Sellers together with my **FREE** gifts. Please also reserve me a special Reader Service subscription. If I decide to subscribe, I shall receive four superb Best Sellers every other month for just £6.40 postage and packing free. If I decide not to subscribe I shall write to you within 10 days. Any **FREE** books and gifts will remain mine to keep. I understand that I am under no obligation whatsoever - I may cancel or suspend my subscription at any time simply by writing to you. *I am over 18 years of age.*

9A2B

MS/MRS/MISS/MR _____

ADDRESS _____

_____

POSTCODE _____ SIGNATURE _____

POST TODAY
and we'll send you this cuddly Teddy Bear.

PLUS a free mystery gift!
we all love mysteries, and so we've an intriguing gift especially for you.

MILLS & BOON
FREEPOST
P.O. BOX 236
CROYDON
CR9 9EL

MAILING PREFERENCE SERVICE

given way to another feeling, a kind of emptiness, a sadness that made the small accomplishments of her day seem drab and colourless. Only feverish, mindless routine could block out her despair.

Nick was true to his word; her contacts with his office had all been through Abdul Gamal or his clerks, and as the days wore on, she became convinced she would never have to see him again, but it was a bitter-sweet comfort. She had succeeded in removing him from her life, yet she found herself looking for his face in every crowd, listening for his voice in every room. There was no logic to it, she told herself in disgust, but there it was. When the local paper ran a photograph of Nick, his smiling face streaked with oil, his hands raised in victory as he sat in a sleek Porsche on a dusty track at Sebring, Florida, all Amanda's eyes could focus on was the shapely red head leaning across his shoulder, handing him the winning trophy. What a man to have been attracted to! she thought, almost angrily. Fast women and fast cars—that was his idea of happiness. She attacked her work with a renewed ferocity that surprised even Helen.

Late one Friday afternoon, the phone rang just as she was concluding some notes for the telex. Helen had already left for the day, and Amanda snatched up the receiver in annoyance at the unwanted interruption. A lump rose into her throat at the sound of an all too familiar voice.

'Good afternoon, Miss Sutton. I'm glad I caught you before you left.'

Amanda ran her tongue over suddenly dry lips and stared at the telephone receiver as if it were alive.

'Are you there, Amanda?' Nick sounded vaguely amused, and she winced as she pictured the expression on his face. 'Or do we have a poor connection?'

'I'm here,' she stammered. 'It's just that I'm surprised

to hear from you. I thought we agreed that Gamal and I would handle things.'

'Yes, we did. Believe me, I wouldn't have called unless it was important. This concerns something you and I have to deal with directly. Do you recall the trip to the construction site we discussed the last time I saw you?'

'Yes,' she said, her mind racing. 'You were going there in a day or two. I assumed. . .'

'Never assume anything, Amanda,' he said casually. 'That's a lesson I learned from you. Actually, I cancelled the trip because other things intervened.'

'Yes, I know,' she said before she could stop herself. 'I saw your picture. Sebring, wasn't it?'

He laughed throatily. 'Yes, that's right. My team took first place. But that wasn't what I meant, Amanda. Much as I love racing, I'd never let it interfere with my business obligations. Actually, I cancelled the desert trip to give my people time to run some preliminary studies.'

'On what?' she asked quickly. 'I've seen the latest figures; the construction is on schedule, isn't it? If there's a problem. . .'

'There's no problem, Amanda, at least none you're responsible for. You see, there's a small town west of the site called El Quamar. It has a small airport, and some of my people have suggested running a road through the desert from there to the site. They think it would be better if we could ship some things in by air. At any rate, I spoke to Tim a while ago and told him I was going out there to check, and he wants you to go with me so you can report back to him. I'm flying out there tonight.'

Grateful that he couldn't see her face, Amanda covered her eyes with her hand and tried to organise her thoughts. There was an insistent pounding in her head and a tightness in her chest. 'I hope you told him that you'd be going without me,' she said, 'because I have no intention of going with you.'

'What was I supposed to tell him, Amanda? That neither one of us wants to be in the company of the other? That wouldn't be something Tim would want to hear from his client, now would it?'

'You could have told him it was unnecessary or that you preferred making the trip alone.'

'Use your head, Amanda,' Nick answered sharply. 'He wants his Olsen & Tibbs representative to file a feasibility report. You are still that representative, aren't you?'

'Yes, of course I am, but this isn't fair.'

Nick laughed harshly. 'You're hardly the person to talk about what's fair or not, are you, Amanda? Or have you put your performance in the garden that night out of your pretty little head altogether? But you don't have anything to worry about; this trip is strictly business. I assure you, I'd much rather be going on this trip alone.'

'Couldn't you make up some excuse?' she asked desperately.

'I could always report my dissatisfaction with you to Tim and request that he send someone to replace you. Would you prefer that?'

'I'd lose my job,' Amanda whispered. 'Surely you wouldn't be so cruel?'

'I'll do whatever needs doing to keep this project on schedule,' Nick answered crisply. 'Just now, I need an authorised Olsen & Tibbs co-ordinator to do an on-site inspection. Pack some things and I'll pick you up in an hour. You'll need enough clothing for a day or two. And I suggest you take along something comfortable for horseback riding.'

'What on earth are you talking about? Won't we be using a jeep or a truck?' Her voice rose in irritation. 'You'll have to make other arrangements, Your

Excellency. I'm not going to ride. . .'

'Nick's laugh sounded brittle to her ears. 'We're going into my territory, Amanda. I'll make the rules.'

There was precious little time in which to hail a cab, get back to the hotel, and pack, but she managed, grimly determined that Nick wouldn't find any reason to criticise her. She had no idea what kind of things to pack, but she wore a khaki trouser suit and sandals, and tossed jeans, cotton shirts, and trainers into a large nylon tote bag. Before the hour was up, Amanda was waiting in front of the hotel, impatiently scanning the sparse traffic for Nick's Rolls-Royce. When a bright red Ferrari screeched to a half in front of her she leaped back, only to realise it was driven by Nick.

'Get in,' he ordered, leaning across the seat and opening the door. 'Don't look so puzzled. I know you thought my chauffeur would drive us, but you were wrong. I keep telling you, Amanda, you mustn't assume anything.'

Her silence was her only answer. In the enforced intimacy of the sports car, she was uncomfortably aware of him. The scent of his cologne drifted through the interior and engulfed her in its light, pleasant aroma. His long legs and broad shoulders threatened to overflow the car's leather seat, and each time he shifted gear his hand brushed against her leg. Amanda tried to stay huddled against the far side of the car, but he took each curve in the road swiftly and she found herself forced nearer to him each time. She stole a discreet glance at him and couldn't help noticing how ruggedly good-looking he was in his tight denim jeans and open-necked shirt. Automatically, her hand went to her hair and patted a few escaped blonde wisps into place. Nick looked at her and grinned.

'You look perfect, as always, although a day or two out

in the desert may rumple you a bit.' His eyes raked over her impersonally. 'Don't you have a hat with you? Well, don't worry, I'm sure we can fix you up with something on the plane. There it is, by the way,' he added, pointing out of the window. 'If we get clearance quickly enough, we should be in El Quamar within the hour.'

The Ferrari screeched to a halt, tossing sand and pebbles into the air. Nick was out of the car in seconds and Amanda followed as rapidly as possible, although the medium high heels of her sandals sank impossibly in the sand beside the runway. Nick paid no attention to her, and she finally pulled off the shoes in disgust and trotted after him, her feet burning in the hot sand. She climbed the access steps to the small, sleek jet that was waiting for them and he took her hand and helped her aboard, but his touch was polite and formal.

'Have you ever flown in one of these before?'

Amanda shook her head, amazed at the jet's luxurious interior. She had expected it to be the same as a commercial jet, except for size, but this was almost like being in someone's living-room. The floor was carpeted in something plush and cushiony, and there were handsome leather chairs and couches instead of rows of hard seats. Nick gestured towards a cupboard along one bulkhead.

'I think you'll be able to find a hat in there,' he said. 'As a matter of fact, take whatever you like. I should have told you to take along a dress for the evening.'

'What evening?' she asked in confusion, but he had already vanished through the door separating the cabin from the cockpit. Amanda went to the closet and found herself confronted by a bewildering assortment of clothing: jeans, dresses, accessories of all sorts, even a flowing fine cotton caftan. The whining hum of jet engines filled the air and she grabbed a wide-brimmed hat from the shelf. At the last moment, almost as an afterthought, she took the caftan from its hanger and added it to the contents of her tote bag. The plane began to move, and she hurried forward to the cockpit. Nick grinned at her from the pilot's seat.

'You look adorable with your mouth hanging open like that, but it hardly suits the executive image you cherish. Sit down and fasten your seatbelt.' He glanced at the hat she held. 'I see you found something for your head,' he remarked.

'Yes,' she answered, easing into the co-pilot's seat. 'You're full of surprises, Your Excellency. I didn't know you had a pilot's licence. And I certainly didn't dream you collected women's clothing!'

'I've had my licence for years,' he said as the earth dipped away beneath them. 'Flying is one of my passions. And you can sheathe your claws, Amanda,' he added, smiling at her. 'This is a corporate jet, and the magazine my conglomerate publishes often uses it to transport staff people for photo layouts. The clothes are for the models' convenience.'

'It really doesn't matter one way or another,' she said stiffly. 'What you do with your life doesn't concern me in the least.'

Nick sighed and checked the gauges on the control panel. 'Look, Amanda, we have an hour or so ahead of us. I like it up here, it's one of the few places I can really unwind, and I refuse to spoil it by sparring with you. So why don't you settle back, enjoy the scenery, and relax? Can you manage that?'

She felt like a child who had been sent to the headmaster's office. Biting back any kind of response, she leaned back in the leather seat. After a while, to her surprise, the smooth drone of the engines and the magnificently blue sky began to soothe her, and she felt herself calmer and more at ease than she had been in days. Nick made only occasional comments, pointing out cloud formation or landmarks in the expanse below. When the plane began a gradual descent she stared out of the window, trying to see El Quamar. At first she saw only endless white sand, then gradually tiny buildings came into view, growing larger as they made their approach to a landing strip that seemed to have come out of nowhere. Effortlessly Nick brought the small jet to a perfect landing.

'El Quamar,' he announced, unbuckling his seatbelt. 'Our stopover for the night.'

'For the night? I thought we were going to the construction site? If you think I'm. . .if you think you. . .if. . .'

'Stop spluttering, Amanda, and listen to me. There's no way to reach the site before nightfall—it's quite a distance from here. We'll leave early in the morning, on horseback. Meanwhile, there's a small hotel here and my company maintains a suite in it. I assure you, you'll be quite comfortable for the night. And you needn't worry, this is strictly business, remember?'

'Just be sure you remember that as well,' she said coolly.

'I never make the same mistake twice,' Nick said quietly.

The hotel was more than he had promised; it was old and charming, with thick white stucco walls which kept out the blazing desert heat. The manager greeted Nick like an old friend and led them to a small but regal suite. With a flourish, Nick whipped open the doors that led off the sitting-room to show her that there were two separate bedrooms.

'Dinner is in a few minutes,' he said, glancing at his watch. 'This is primarily a company town—lots of

mineral and oil exploration, and there's usually a group
of archaeologists passing through. I think you'll enjoy the
evening. There's just time to shower and change.' Nick
smiled slightly and dropped her tote bag on a chair. 'If
you had the good sense to take a caftan from the plane, I
think you might find it appropriate.'

Amanda blushed as he closed her door after him. He
seemed to know every move she made, but she had to
admit that the thin caftan she had taken with her was
beautiful. Long, flowing, feeling more like silk than
cotton, it clung subtly yet provocatively to the contours
of her body. Its pale violet and blue stripes brought out
the colour of her eyes and made her blonde hair look ever
more bright and golden in colour than usual. Somehow it
seemed just right for this place, she thought musingly as
she gazed out of the window to where a group of tall palm
trees bent in a gentle wind. She brushed her hair into a
halo of soft curls, then caught the sides back in a blue
ribbon.

Even Nick's expression softened at the sight of her
when she opened her door. As he took her down to
the dining-room, the silence between them seemed
heightened by the way he kept looking at her.

'You look lovely,' he said at last, and she managed a
polite smile in return.

'Thank you. It's a beautiful caftan. Whoever left it
behind has good taste.'

'That's very generous of you, Amanda, but it's you
who makes the caftan beautiful.' He put his hand on her
arm and turned to face her. 'Amanda, we're going to
spend a lot of time together the next day or two. Why
don't we start over? Perhaps we've misunderstood each
other. Wouldn't it be easier if we were friends instead of
adversaries?'

His words seemed sincere and, for a second, she was

tempted to respond in kind. But there was an intensity in his face and in the touch of his hand on her skin that made her feel lightheaded, and she drew back.

'We can be compatible business associates,' she said coolly. 'That is what you meant, isn't it?'

Instantly his face hardened. 'Of course, Amanda. That's precisely what I meant,' he said quickly, but there was a flicker of something she couldn't immediately identify in his voice. With amazement, she realised she had hurt him. Strangely, the knowledge brought with it no feeling of satisfaction, and she reached out towards him.

'Nick—' she began, but he brushed past her and the moment of intimacy was gone. She felt a peculiar, numbing sense of loss as she followed him into the dining room. At once they were surrounded by a laughing, chattering group of men and women.

A large, burly man with a drooping moustache embraced Nick in a bear-hug. 'We heard you'd arrived, Nick. It's a long time since we've seen you around here. How are you?'

'It's good to see you, George. Where's Elaine?'

The man looked around and drew a pert woman towards him. 'Here she is now,' he said. 'Elaine, love, say hello to Nick.'

'You look beautiful as always, Elaine,' said Nick, bending to kiss her cheek.

'And you're still the same charming liar you always were, Nicky,' she laughed, kissing him back. She peered near-sightedly at Amanda. 'Aren't you going to introduce us to this young woman?' she demanded.

'Amanda Sutton, may I introduce George and Elaine Dunhill? They're old friends of mine. George is a mining engineer from the States.'

George Dunhill chuckled and shook Amanda's outstretched hand. 'That's right, Miss Sutton. It's always a pleasure to meet a fellow American in the midst of all this confounded sand.'

'Now, George,' his wife chided gently, 'the poor girl hasn't said a word yet—not that we've given her much of a chance. Perhaps she's not American after all.'

'Oh, I am, Mrs Dunhill. I guess it's obvious.'

'Nothing is obvious out here, Amanda. You don't mind if I call you by your first name, do you? There doesn't seem to be much call for formality in this town. I mean, we know just about everybody, anyway.'

'Have you been here long?' Amanda asked politely.

'Oh, about five years, I guess. Isn't that right, George? We're from Denver, originally, but we've bounced around a lot since we've been married. What brings you to our little desert hideaway?' Elaine glanced at Nick and laughed. 'Or shouldn't I ask?'

'Amanda is with Olsen & Tibbs, the firm building the irrigation project out at Marakef. She's here on business. In fact, she's one of their most conscientious employees, isn't that right, Amanda?'

Amanda felt a knot of irritation tighten within her. The Dunhills looked from Nick to her in puzzled silence. 'That's right, Nick,' she said pleasantly. 'This is strictly business for me.'

'You mean you're here with Nick as part of your job?' George Dunhill asked, barely restraining the glee in his voice.

'Oh, George, don't be so smug!' scolded his wife, poking her elbow in her husband's ribs. 'Don't pay any attention to him, Amanda—he loves to tease. But that does explain why you're so refreshingly different from Nicky's usual dates.'

Her husband burst out laughing. 'Well, that's putting it bluntly!' he gasped, patting his wife on the back.

Elaine blushed. 'That's truthful, not blunt, George. I just meant you're not hanging all over Nicky, playing the role of helpless female. You understand, don't you?'

Amanda smiled and stole a glance at Nick, but his expression was unreadable. 'I do indeed,' she said, 'and I thank you for the compliment.'

Elaine turned to Nick and stared at him. 'Business or not,' she said, 'if you're smart, you'll hang on to this one.' Then she linked her arm with Amanda's. 'Come on, dear, and I'll introduce you to the rest of the crazies who live in this last outpost of the civilised world.'

There were enough people gathered at the bar and at the tables so that Amanda soon gave up trying to remember all their names. It was an interesting mix of people from differing fields, from all parts of the globe. She could see Nick moving from group to group, being greeted warmly by everyone. There was a party atmosphere in the room, and Elaine explained that the group gathered almost every Friday evening. In one corner there was an old record player, and a seemingly endless stack of records was being played on it. Someone urged a plateful of lamb and couscous on her, and she had barely tasted it before someone else whisked her off to the tiny dance-floor. From time to time she caught a glimpse of Nick, who was tall enough to stand out in spite of the group gathered around him, but he never seemed to look in her direction. In fact, although it seemed that every man in the room wanted to dance with her, Nick never came near. She'd really done it, she thought; he'd finally lost interest in her. Yet somehow it seemed an empty victory. There was no feeling of triumph or elation. In fact, as the evening wore on, she became more and more distressed by his indifference, and when at last she saw him coming towards her from across the crowded room, she turned all her attention to the young geologist next to

her. She pretended to be surprised when Nick took her
arm politely and drew her aside.

'I'm sorry it's taken me so long to get to you, Amanda.'

'That's OK,' she said brightly. 'Everyone is very
friendly. You needn't worry about me.'

Another record dropped on to the turntable and the
slow, dreamy strains of 'Stardust' filled the room.
Amanda began to hum along with the music, and Nick
smiled at her.

'That old tune is pretty, isn't it?' he asked.

'Yes,' she said softly, wondering if he would take her
into his arms, 'It's lovely to dance to.'

Nick smiled politely. 'Well, I'm sure you'll find
someone to enjoy it with. I'm going to step outside for a
few minutes and check on something.'

'Is it about the trip to the irrigation project?' she
asked. 'Can I help?'

'No, no, it has nothing to do with that. You just stay
here and enjoy yourself. A friend of mine wants to show
me some seismological tracings she's made. She thinks
they might indicate an oil deposit.'

He turned as a woman's voice called his name and
waved his hand at a tall, attractive brunette who smiled
and nodded.

'Is that her?' Amanda asked politely. 'Your friend, I
mean.'

'Yes, that's Susannah. You don't mind, do you?' he
asked pleasantly. 'It'll only take us a few minutes.'

'Why should I mind?' she asked coolly, choking back
the disappointment she felt. 'We're here on business,
aren't we? What you do isn't any of my concern.'

'I simply thought you might wonder where I'd gone.'
he said patiently, smiling at her. 'I didn't want you to
worry.'

'Worry?' she repeated. 'I doubt if I'd even have

noticed that you'd left.'

The smile left his face and he looked at her with cool detachment. 'Well then, I won't bother you any more, Amanda. I guess that's one of the benefits of being—how did you phrase it?—compatible business associates, isn't it?'

She turned away from him without answering and walked towards a man who had been staring at her earlier in the evening. 'Have we met?' she asked, hoping Nick could hear every word. 'I'm Amanda Sutton.' When she looked back, Nick was gone.

For several minutes she kept up a pleasant, casual conversation with the young man. He was an archaeology student, he told her, passing through El Quamar on a field trip. If he was aware that Amanda's eyes kept searching the room for Nick, he made no mention of it.

'Have you seen the ruins here?' he asked after a moment.

'Ruins?' Amanda repeated, trying to force her attention to what he'd been saying. 'No, I haven't. I didn't even know there were any.'

'There's an old fort just outside the hotel,' he said. 'They say it dates all the way from the time of the Crusades. I'm going to take a good look at it in the morning, but I thought I'd take a peek at it tonight. Would you like to join me?'

'No, I don't think so,' Amanda replied. 'Thanks anyway.'

'We'd only be gone a few minutes,' the man said. When she didn't answer, he shrugged. 'Well, of course, if you think the Sheikh might object. . .'

The sentence trailed off into silence, and Amanda flushed. 'I'm not answerable to him or anyone,' she retorted angrily as she slipped her arm through his. 'On second thoughts, I'd love to see the ruins.'

Outside the hotel, the desert sky was like a black sea filled with a million gleaming pinpoints of light. A crescent moon barely illuminated a crumbling pile of stone set a short distance from the hotel. Amanda paused on the steps of the building and shivered in the cool night air.

'It's terribly dark,' she said doubtfully. 'Perhaps I'll wait until morning.'

'You'll be able to see more clearly once your eyes adjust to the darkness,' the young man said, urging her forward. 'We're almost there.'

They were walking rapidly out of the warm glow of light from the hotel; finally, only darkness surrounded them. Amanda was suddenly very aware of the force of the man's hand on her arm and the silence.

'I guess you have to be a scholar to appreciate this,' she said nervously. 'Look, I don't want to spoil this for you. You stay as long as you like, I'm going to go back to the hotel.'

The man muttered something and pulled her roughly towards him. His grip was like iron and she could smell the odour of liquor on his breath. She tried desperately to push him away, and her fear turned to terror as she realised she was losing the struggle.

'Let go of me!' she shouted, but his only answer was to force her further into the shadows cast by the ruins.

'Don't scream,' he snarled, clamping his hand over her mouth. His heavy body pinned her against a cold stone wall and he began to fumble roughly at the neck of her caftan. Then, incredibly, he seemed to stagger backwards. It took Amanda a second to realise that someone had grabbed the young man by the neck and pulled him from her. It was Nick, and in one smooth motion he stepped in front of her and hit her attacker on the jaw. The man crumbled and fell to the ground.

'Are you all right, Amanda? Did he hurt you?'

'I'm fine,' she gasped, trying to stop shaking. 'Only frightened. Thank God you found us! I don't know what would have happened if you hadn't.'

'I do,' Nick said grimly. He stripped off his jacket and wrapped it around her shoulders. 'Here,' he said gruffly, 'you're shaking. What the devil are you doing out here with this. . .this thing?' he growled, nudging the fallen figure with his foot.

'I came out to see the ruins of the fort,' she said, beginning to cry. 'He invited me.'

'He invited me,' Nick mocked sarcastically, and she flinched at the angry tone of his voice. 'How could you have been so stupid?' He grasped her shoulders and shook her. 'Didn't you think? Didn't you?'

'Nick, please,' she sobbed, 'you're hurting me. It isn't my fault this happened.'

He stepped back and took a deep breath. Then, as the man on the ground began to moan, he looked away from her. 'Go on up to the suite, Amanda,' he said sharply. 'Go on,' he repeated, pushing her roughly towards the pathway. 'At once, Amanda, or I'll be as angry with you as I am with him!'

With a muffled cry, she turned and fled towards the hotel. Praying not to meet anyone, she hurried up the stairs to their rooms. Once safely inside, she sat huddled in a chair in the darkness, until eventually the door opened and Nick entered. He came to her side and knelt beside her.

'Are you sure you're all right, little one?' He reached out and gently wiped the tears from her face. 'I should turn you over my knee and spank you for having been so foolish!'

'Don't you scold me,' she sobbed, turning her face away from him. 'I didn't do anything wrong—it was that

horrible man who's to blame. Do you think I wanted him
to try to do those things to me? How could you think
such an awful thing?'

'Amanda, hush,' whispered Nick, gently putting a
finger across her mouth. 'I'm sorry you had such a
terrible experience, and I'm sorrier still if I upset you.
But when I think of what might have happened to
you. . .Amanda, what on earth possessed you? Why did
you go out there with a man you'd only just met?'

'He said he was an archaeologist, and anyway all those
people were friends of yours—at least, I thought they
were. Besides, you and that woman were. . .were. . .'

She started to cry again, and Nick smoothed the
tousled hair back from her flushed cheeks. 'I told you
Susannah and I were going to look at some read-outs,
Amanda. Didn't you believe me? Were you jealous?' he
asked gently as he stroked her face. 'Tell me.'

'It doesn't matter,' she said tiredly.

Nick was touching her as gently as if she were an
exhausted child. 'It matters to me,' he said softly.
'Everything about you matters to me, Amanda. Haven't
you realised that yet?'

She looked directly at him, surprised and touched by
the compassion and concern in his face and voice. The
quiet intensity of the moment seemed to hang suspended
between them, until she closed her tear-dampened eyes
and sighed. 'I'm exhausted, Nick. I just can't seem to
think straight any more.'

'I understand, little one. We don't have to talk any
more tonight. . .but there's something I have to tell you.'
He lifted her face to him and smiled at her. 'I'm sorry
about that last time we were together—not for wanting to
make love to you, Amanda, but for all the things we said
later. I don't believe any of them—I don't think I
believed them, even then.'

'I didn't mean any of it, Nick,' she whispered, too weary and drained to lie any more. 'I'm so sorry.'

He smiled and shook his head. 'There's nothing to apologise for, little one. I just want you to be honest from now on, with yourself and with me. It's not a sign of weakness to want to be loved, you know. That wall you've built around yourself may keep you safe, Amanda, but it also keeps you trapped in loneliness.'

'I'm not lonely,' she insisted, turning her face from him. 'I have my career.'

'I told you before, Amanda,' he said softly, 'be honest for both our sakes.'

He was so close to her that she could feel his warm breath on her cheek. She wanted to tell him the truth, to explain that the wall she had built was her protection, the only defence she had against ever again experiencing the pain she'd gone through with Todd. She couldn't deceive herself any longer, she knew. What she felt for Nick was more than temporary physical passion; she knew without question that if she gave herself to him the carefully created woman she had worked so hard to become would be destroyed if he left her. And yet how else could it end? She knew the kind of man he was. . .there was no way to explain without losing the little pride she had left. She stirred in the chair and moved away from him.

'Please, Nick,' she whispered, 'I'm too tired to argue with you.'

Before she could protest he had scooped her up into his arms. 'You're right, little one,' he said, 'we can talk tomorrow.'

Holding her as carefully as if she was made of fragile crystal, he carried her into her bedroom and placed her gently on the bed. He knelt and removed her sandals, brushing the sand from her feet.

'Don't, please,' she murmured, but he ignored her,

untying the ribbon from her hair so it fell free on the pillow. He had not turned on the lights, and there was only enough moonlight in the darkened room to make shadowy figures of them both. Strangely soothed and comforted by the darkness, Amanda raised her arms obediently as Nick pulled her caftan over her head. An electric current of anticipation ran through her, and she knew he felt it too because she could hear his quickened breath as the gown came free, but his hands didn't touch her body. Tense with growing excitement, unsure of what she wanted him to do, she waited, not daring to move, her skin tingling in a thousand different places. Wordlessly, Nick covered her with a thin cotton sheet and tucked it around her protectively. Only then did his fingers gently trail a delicate, burning path down her body, from breasts to hip, over the thin covering.

'Nick,' she whispered, unable to say more.

'Good night, little one,' he murmured huskily, and brushed his lips gently against hers, the touch so light it was like a kiss in a dream. 'Sleep well.'

'Nick,' she whispered again, but the door had closed and he was gone.

CHAPTER SEVEN

A HOT desert breeze whispered through the open window the next morning as Amanda awoke to the ringing of the telephone. It was Nick, who sounded as if he had been up for hours.

'I'm downstairs getting some things together for our trip,' he told her. 'I didn't have the heart to wake you earlier. I looked in on you, but you were still sound asleep. How do you feel this morning?'

'I'm fine, thank you,' she said, colouring as she remembered how he had put her to bed the night before. 'Do I have time for coffee?'

'Just barely, Amanda. There's a carafe waiting for you in the sitting room. I'll give you just fifteen minutes to get down here. And Amanda, you'll find a saddlebag near the coffee service. Just stuff in some extra shirts and a jacket, whatever you think you'll need.'

'You weren't kidding, were you?' she said in some surprise. 'We're really going to ride.'

'Don't sound so terrified!' he laughed. 'I've got a very gentle mare for you.'

As usual, she found herself rushing to meet Nick's deadline. By the time she reached the early morning quiet of the lobby, she was eager to get started, but to her disappointment Nick was nowhere to be seen. The only other person in the lobby was a Bedouin in long white robes who stood near the doorway. At the sound of her footsteps he turned, and she was shocked to see that it was Nick. He was so fierce-looking, so tanned and lean in his white robe, that her pulse quickened at the sight. He grinned at her, his white, even teeth a startling contrast against his sun-darkened face.

'I should have warned you, Amanda,' he said, laughing at her obvious surprise. 'I don't know if it's habit or not, but I'm more comfortable in the desert if I'm dressed this way. Are you ready? We have a long way to travel.'

As he had promised, a gentle Arab mare was waiting for her at the back of the hotel. They started down a narrow track leading into the desert scrub. For the first few miles they rode slowly while Amanda concentrated on recalling her riding skills, although the well-trained mare seemed to anticipate every command. As Amanda began to relax, Nick pointed out things in the landscape that were completely unexpected: occasional patches of brilliantly coloured wildflowers, soaring vultures, even the tiny, almost invisible tracks of a desert fox. There was an easy companionship between them that reminded her of their impromptu picnic weeks before. The heat of the sun, the blue of the endless sky, seemed to fill her with happiness. Once Nick pointed to a faint grey smudge on the horizon.

'It would take too long to ride there, but that's what's left of a walled city, Amanda. It's at least five hundred years old—a real ruin.' He laughed, and she couldn't help but laugh along with him, remembering how easily she had been fooled the previous night.

At midday, just when she had begun to ache from the unaccustomed strain of riding, with the blazing sun beginning to beat down unmercifully on them, he pointed again to a blur ahead.

'Le Restaurant Bedouin,' he said, smiling at her. 'An oasis,' he explained, 'and a beautiful one. We'll have lunch under the palm trees and rest for a while.'

The indistinct blur seemed to shimmer in the sun,

gradually changing from a hazy, greenish outline to a series of tall palms carpeted by lush green grass. There was a faint scent of water in the still, hot air, and the horses must have smelled it, too, because suddenly both of them began to gallop. Amanda laughed as her little mare raced ahead of Nick's big stallion, and she reached the oasis and scampered off the animal's back seconds ahead of him.

'I win!' she cried, clapping her hands with delight. 'Oh Nick, this place is magnificent!'

The oasis was like a magic kindgom, set in the midst of endless white sand. Overhanging palms shielded the sweet-smelling grass from the hot sun, and set in its emerald-green centre was a pool of sapphire-blue water. The mare and the stallion had their muzzles deep in the water before Amanda knelt on the mossy bank and plunged her hand into the blue depths.

'It's freezing!' she gasped as the icy drops hit her sunwarmed skin.

'And delicious,' added Nick, scooping some into his cupped hand. He laughed when she tried to imitate him unsuccessfully, and he scooped up another handful of water and offered it to her. She bent towards him and her mouth brushed against his hand as she drank. There was something so intimate, so sensual at the unexpected contact of his hot skin against her lips that she flinched and drew back. The sound of his laughter died away, and she looked up, determined to meet his eyes, but it was impossible. There was such a wild, intense look in their blue depths that it was like a physical blow. Quickly she rose to her feet.

'You said something about lunch, Nick. I hope you meant it, because I'm starving!'

'Amanda. . .'

'I haven't had this much exercise in a long time,' she

babbled nervously. 'I only had coffee for beakfast.'

'Amanda, please listen to me,' he said, taking her gently by the shoulders. 'I want to set things straight between us, once and for all. Last night I realised how really naïve and vulnerable you are under that tough exterior you've cultivated. I don't know who hurt you, or how, but locking your feelings within yourself isn't the way to handle the problem.'

'There is no problem,' she said, her voice barely a whisper.

'Don't try to tell me that,' he said quietly. 'You're a vibrant, lovely woman, and you're too intelligent to believe that, or to expect me to believe it, either. You can't fool me, Amanda,' he insisted, 'even though you keep trying.' He tilted her chin up and smiled at her. 'Why won't you trust me, little one?' he whispered. 'Or is it yourself you don't trust?'

'I don't understand what's happening,' she admitted, tears suddenly filling her eyes. 'I'm afraid.'

'Of what?' he whispered, drawing her into his arms. 'I'll never hurt you, little one, don't you know that?' Gently his mouth claimed hers. His lips, his hands, were soft and tender upon her. She was incapable of thought, and her hands stole up to touch his face, his hair, and all at once his kiss changed, became fierce and demanding, and something deep within her stirred. She sighed against his eager mouth as her soft lips parted under the passionate strength of his. He tasted sweet and wonderful, and her senses were flooded with him, his clean, sunwarmed smell, the heat of his hands on her, the hardness of his body against hers. Nick unclasped the clip in her hair and when the long golden strands fell free he caught its silky weight in his hand, pulling her head back so that her smooth throat was bared to the touch of his lips. Amanda wanted to call out, to stop him, but she could only whisper his name over and over, and she wrapped her slender arms around his neck and moulded her body to his, her breasts taut against his chest, her thighs tight against his male hardness.

Nick whispered her name and his hands began to move on her body, caressing her breasts, stroking the soft line from her waist to her curving hips. Every place he touched felt as if it were aflame, and she clung tightly to him. His hand had moved under her cotton shirt, exploring her back, and she felt as if each pore in her naked skin was springing to life under his stroking fingers. The sand seemed to be shifting beneath her feet. It was as if she were spinning in space, as if she were drowning, and when Nick lifted her into his arms she clung tightly to him. He carried her away from the water's edge and laid her down gently on the soft grass beneath a sighing palm tree, never taking his mouth from hers. Her hands moved over his face, his strong shoulders, his back, wanting to feel every part of him, to touch every inch of his lean, hard body, and when he began to unbutton her blouse she murmured his name and buried her fingers in the thick, curling hair at the nape of his neck. Nick's lips traced a line of gentle kisses from the pulsing hollow of her throat to the shadowed cleft between her breasts. She whimpered when his tongue touched the soft flesh swelling above her bra as he cupped her breast in his hand. Somehow, he slipped the blouse from her shoulders, and when his mouth touched the lacy fabric of her bra Amanda's hands guided him and pressed his face to her breasts. She could feel them swelling, aching to be free of their flimsy covering, eagerly awaiting his touch, and when he lifted her gently towards him and reached for her bra clasp she arched upwards, her compliant body helping him, urging him to remove the unwanted covering between them. Nick

tossed the bra aside and she moaned as his mouth closed
over one alabaster breast, crying out in ecstasy as his
tongue and teeth toyed lovingly with the delicate nipple.
His hand was on her other breast, stroking it tenderly,
teasing the erect nerve-endings to flame. She buried her
face in his neck, kissing his throat, tasting his warm,
supple flesh. Dimly she heard him repeating her name in
a choked whisper, then he leaned back and looked down
at her sunkissed, love-dampened body. 'You're so
lovely,' he whispered, and she glowed at the tenderness
in his face. She reached up to him, wanting him back in
her arms, aching for the feel of his hands, his lips, and he
bent and kissed her again, his mouth encircling her
passion-bruised lips. His hands were moving slowly
down her eager body, and then she felt them on her hips,
touching, stroking, opening her jeans, easing them past
her hips, and she froze at the sudden realisation of what
was about to happen. 'Don't!' she cried, beginning to
struggle beneath him. 'Nick, you can't!'

And then she was truly afraid of him. He stared at her,
all the softness gone from his face, his icy blue eyes
narrowed into cat-like slits. As she raised her hands,
frantically pushing against his chest, he grasped both her
wrists in one strong hand and drew her arms up over her
head.

'I can, little one,' he growled hoarsely. 'For once in
your life, stop thinking. Just feel, Amanda. Feel what
I'm doing, and you'll know it's what you've wanted me to
do since the moment we met.'

He knelt above her, blocking out the sky and hot sun.
With one hand he pulled the denim jeans from her, and
she cried out. His eyes seemed to consume her as he bent
slowly and kissed her breasts. Slowly, his lips moved down
her writhing body, touching her soft flesh. His breath
was warm on her navel, on the flat plane of her stomach.

She struggled in his powerful grip, but it was futile.

'Nick,' she sobbed helplessly as his hand moved over her bikini panties, brushing lightly over the slightly mounded surface, 'Nick. . .' but his fingers closed over the lacy waistband, removing the final flimsy covering, and her body was betraying her, no longer struggling against him but arching up to his. And then she was naked in the sun, and he murmured her name, he was gathering her to him, and her wrists were free, her hands were free, free to hit him, to fight him—but she was lost, beyond rational thought, beyond fear, and her arms wound tightly around his neck. She whispered his name against his mouth as his white robe fell to the grass.

His body was beautiful to her eyes, from his broad, muscular shoulders to his lean, tapered hips. Her hands moved lightly, wonderingly over his hard shoulders and back, feeling the muscles moving smoothly under his silky-hot skin. His mouth found her breast, and as she cried out in pleasure at the touch of his lips and teeth, his hand moved gently across her hips to her silken thighs and finally found the moist, hidden centre of her. She sobbed out his name and his hands moved beneath her yielding body, lifting her to him. His lips covered hers, and they joined together.

It was like nothing she had ever known before, not during the months with Todd, not even in her wildest hidden dreams. She felt as though she were dying and being reborn all at the same time as they moved together in passionate embrace. She wanted to become part of Nick, to be one with his flesh everywhere they touched, and her mouth and breasts and thighs strained to meet his. And as they soared upward together, as the rapture they shared transported her to a place she had never before been, she called out his name. His mouth became savage on hers, and they were one.

CHAPTER EIGHT

WHEN Amanda finally became aware of the passage of time she was lying in Nick's arms, her head nestled against his chest. She could hear the strong, steady beat of his heart, and she sighed with contentment and snuggled closer to him under the white robe he had drawn over their love-spent bodies.

'Are you awake?' he whispered as she stirred, and she caught her breath, suddenly overcome by shyness. 'I know you are,' he said teasingly, 'because you've stopped snoring.'

'Nick!' She rolled away and sat up, the robe falling to her waist. 'That's absolutely untrue. I don't snore. What a terrible thing to say!'

He laughed and rolled on his side. 'It was just a joke, little one. I couldn't resist teasing you.'

The smile faded from his face as his eyes travelled slowly down her body, pausing at her exposed breasts; he reached towards her and his fingertips brushed one taut nipple, and she drew in her breath sharply, amazed by the swift intensity of her response to his touch. She could see the male hardness of him stirring under the white robe and she leaped to her feet like a skittish doe.

'I'm all covered with sand,' she said. She felt vulnerable and embarrassed by her naked body and she turned away from him. 'I'm going to take a swim.'

Nick watched her and then a smile creased his tanned face and he got to his feet. It's going to be cold,' he warned. 'Are you sure you want to do that?'

With a nod of her head, Amanda ran splashing

through the shallows into the deeper water of the pool. The icy shock of the water was enough to make her cry out, and she hesitated. But suddenly Nick was beside her, laughing aloud, and he grabbed her hands and pulled her further into the pool.

'Nick, don't!' she screamed. 'It's so cold I can't bear it!'

He grinned and disappeared beneath the water. Seconds later his hand encircled her ankle, and he pulled her under the water with him. She pulled free and surfaced, spluttering and laughing, everything forgotten but the fun of the game.

'I can play rough, too,' she warned, and splashed water in his face.

They frolicked together like two children, ducking each other and shrieking with laughter. Then, after a while, Amanda became more and more aware of the liquid caress of Nick's wet body against hers, and she felt his hands lingering sensually on her wet skin. Their laughter died suddenly and she turned and swam towards the edge of the pool. Her heart was beating rapidly as she reached the shallow water and she could sense Nick's presence behind her. Suddenly his arms were around her and he drew her back against him.

'Don't run away from me, Amanda,' he murmured, and the words seemed as much a warning as an invitation. She felt weak at his touch and she moaned helplessly as she felt the hardness of him stirring against her. His hands cupped her wet breasts, his thumbs moving slowly and awakening their pink tips. She shivered expectantly as he kissed her neck, lingering in the soft hollow at her shoulder, then burning a trail of soft kisses to her ear lobe, and she turned in his arms and raised her open mouth to his. She clutched at him fiercely, her hands urging him closer to her, and she raised herself to him.

She felt like a flower whose petals were opening slowly
to the caress of the hot summer sun, revealing the sweet,
hidden nectar of herself. Nick whispered words she
couldn't understand as he kissed her and stroked her.
She was adrift in time and space, aware of nothing but
her need to touch him and be touched by him. With a sob
she gave herself up again to this man who had conquered
her, who had won a greater victory than he could
possibly know. Like a leaf torn free in a windstorm, she
was carried aloft by their passion.

At last, as the fiery sun dipped low in the opalescent
blue sky, they dressed in silence and re-saddled their
horses. There seemed no need for words as they rode
slowly into the ancient desert sands. There was a great
feeling of peace and security within Amanda, and she
glanced at Nick from under lowered lashes from time to
time, as if to reassure herself that he was real. She felt she
could go on in this dream for ever, and when he finally
reined in the stallion and pointed towards the west she
was almost disappointed.

'You mean we've arrived at Marakef already?' She
shielded her eyes and stared into the distance. 'I can't see
anything, Nick. Are those tents past that dune? Nick,
where are we?'

He laughed at her bewildered expression. 'No, it's
not Marakef, Amanda. You might call it a Bedouin
encampment. Do you remember the Harrows? You met
them at my house a few weeks ago. Our public health
service sent Charlie out here to vaccinate the crew at the
construction site, and Shalal came along with him.
They're both amateur archaeologists and there's a
marvellous old ruin not far from here, so they decided to
camp out for a couple of days. I told them we'd be
coming this way and they invited us to spend the night—

that is, unless you prefer not to.'

Amanda hesitated while the little mare danced impatiently beneath her. 'You mean they know I'm with you? What will they think? About us, I mean.'

Nick reached out and touched her hair gently. 'I told them we'd be travelling together on business, Amanda. Anyway, they're my friends, not judge and jury. And we have nothing to hide, have we?'

'No,' she answered impulsively. 'And I'd love to camp in the desert.'

'Then what are we waiting for?' Nick urged his horse to a gallop and Amanda followed. As they rode in, Charlie and Shalal emerged from one of the tents. They both waved and called out greetings.

Shalal welcomed Amanda with a hug and a warm smile. 'We're so glad to see you,' she said. 'And your timing is perfect; Charlie was just about to make us some drinks.'

Amanda looked around the encampment with interest, at the three large conical-shaped tents, the folding canvas chairs, the small table.

'It looks a bit like a set from *Lawrence of Arabia*, doesn't it?' laughed Shalal. 'But don't let appearances fool you, Amanda. We have all the civilised refinements, including ice and caviare. It's not quite the miracle it seems—we have a jeep parked back there, and it only takes half an hour to get to Marakef.'

Amanda turned to Nick and he smiled at the unspoken question in her eyes. 'We can stay here as long as you like, Amanda,' he said softly. 'I'm in no rush to get to work, and I'm sure the Harrows won't mind.'

'We're delighted to have company, aren't we, Shalal?' Charlie asked, and his wife beamed agreeably.

'Absolutely, Charlie. Why don't you stir up something cold for us while I put the finishing touches to dinner?

Nick, Amanda can use that far tent. Perhaps she'd like to wash before we eat.'

'Oh, I would. I feel as if I'm covered with sand everywhere!' Amanda blushed at the sound of her own words as Nick took her hand and led her away. 'I wonder what the Harrows think, Nick? I mean, Shalal kept looking at us strangely.'

'They know we came out here on business, Amanda. But if they think we're lovers, does it matter? Don't tell me you regret what happened between us.'

'No,' she said in a soft voice, 'I don't regret it. Nick, don't!' she added as he drew her towards him. 'The Harrows. . .'

Nick laughed and stepped back. 'All right, little one, I don't want to upset you. But I'm sure neither Charlie nor Shalal would be shocked if they saw me kiss you. All right, all right, I'll behave,' he added hastily as she started to argue. 'I think you'll find a washbasin and towels in your tent. Unless you'd like me to stay and help you with those buttons. . .'

Amanda blushed and gently pushed him from the tent entrance. 'You're terrible!' she whispered.

He blew her a kiss and walked off. There was, as he had promised, a basin of water in which to wash. In fact, the tent contained all the things necessary for comfort, including a small mirror in which Amanda checked her face and hair after she had washed and changed into a fresh cotton sweater. By the time she emerged from the tent, night was falling on the campsite. Charles had lit Coleman lanterns near the tents, and Shalal placed flickering candles on the table. There was a variety of delicious food and drink, so much so that Amanda groaned when Shalal tried to urge dessert on her.

'I couldn't eat another bite, Shalal, thank you just the

same. I'm not even sure I can move! Let me help you clean up.'

Shalal laughed and shook her head. 'That's the best thing about this kind of holiday, Amanda. I put away the leftovers, and Charlie does everything else. But I'd be delighted if you kept me company while I sort these things out.'

In the soft glow of candlelight, while Nick went to see to the horses, Amanda and the older woman chatted quietly. Shalal was charming and friendly, and Amanda found herself drawn to her. Shalal spoke lovingly of her husband and her career. Then suddenly she paused in her work and stared at Amanda.

'I hope you don't mind my saying so, but you seem different from when we first met.'

Amanda hoped the flickering light disguised the rush of colour she felt in her face. Could the hours spent in Nick's arms have made a visible difference? As if she had read her thoughts, Shalal chuckled.

'I only meant you seem more relaxed and at ease. The night we met, I thought I sensed a certain antagonism between you and Nicky.' There was the barest hint of a smile on her pleasant face. 'Now, I get the feeling you've grown to like each other. I certainly hope so. Nicky is a wonderful man, Amanda. I've never seen him so comfortable with a woman before.'

Amanda felt her heart soar within her. 'Do you really mean that?'

'I've known Nicky for years, Amanda, and I've seen him with quite a few women.' Shalal glanced sideways at Amanda. 'I'm not telling you anything you didn't really know, am I?' she asked, but it was more a statement of fact than a question.

'I know about his reputation, Shalal, if that's what you're asking,' Amanda said steadily.

'His reputation is largely a creation of the gossip-mongers, Amanda. Nicky is young, handsome; his business and his racing keep him in the public eye. All he has to do is smile at a woman and the scandal sheets claim he's made another conquest. The truth is, his work has been his life, but that doesn't make good copy for the magazines, does it? I used to think there was no time in his life for a real relationship, but I finally realised he's just never met the right woman, one who can love him for what he is and not what he's accomplished. And he needs someone like that, someone he can love, you know.'

There was silence between the two women. Only the distant sounds of a night bird drifted to them on a gentle breeze, along with the faint sounds of the horses neighing. Amanda looked across the table at Shalal, but could read nothing in her face.

'Why are you telling me all this?' she asked.

Shalal looked at her shrewdly. 'I get the feeling there's something special between you two. Is there? I know it's none of my business, but. . .'

'There's an expression women use a lot but never mean,' said Charlie, walking into the glow of the candlelight. 'Have I disrupted some important girl talk?' He looked at his wife, who sighed and rolled her eyes up in exaggerated despair.

'Your timing is terrible, Charlie! Of course you have, but I suppose it's just as well—I was about to be a meddlesome busybody. Charlie, where's that old guitar of yours? You've got a captive audience here. Aren't you going to make the most of it?'

The night was bitterly cold, but Amanda knew she had never been as happy before. The desert sky was a black velvet cloth studded with billions of silver lights, and Nick built a warming fire around which they all huddled.

In spite of Shalal's teasing, Charlie brought out his guitar and his surprisingly fine baritone led them in a series of old, familiar songs. It seemed the most natural thing in the world to lean back in Nick's arms, snug against the cold and comforted by his very presence. Eventually, when everyone had said good night, Nick walked a yawning Amanda to her tent. She stopped him as he started to pull back the door flap.

'You can't sleep in here, Nick. What will the Harrows think?'

'Amanda, you must be joking! First of all, I don't care what they think. And secondly, I suspect they've figured it out by now. We're not exactly children, little one.'

'Nick, I couldn't! I'd never be able to face them in the morning. There's a third tent,' she pleaded. 'Can't you sleep in there?'

'In the supply tent, with the pots and pans?' Nick sighed and kissed her gently on the tip of the nose. 'I suppose so. But you'll owe me for this,' he warned. 'And I'll demand repayment.'

Amanda smiled to herself in the darkness. 'I'll look forward to it,' she murmured. She stood on tiptoe, kissed him quickly, and slipped into the tent.

By the dim beam of a flashlight she undressed quickly, shivering in the cold. There was a warm down sleeping-bag spread on top of a pile of soft cushions, and she snuggled into it gratefully and switched off the flashlight. The darkness was impenetrable, so deep and complete that it was like an unseen presence weighing down on her. Somewhere in the vast desert a strange animal called out, and the hair on the back of her neck rose. In spite of her exhaustion, she doubted that she would be able to sleep. Although her eyes were wide open, she couldn't see a thing, and she could hear the sound of her own heart thumping in the eerie stillness. She couldn't think of any animals that might be prowling about outside, but every rustle, every slight sound made her jump. She told herself there was nothing to fear out here, but an unbidden vision of the night before, when she had been lured out into the darkness and attacked, flashed into her mind, and she shuddered and burrowed deeper into the down bag. There was a soft, sudden sound from the door of the tent, followed by a slight stir of cold air, and Amanda sat up, terrified, the cover dropping to her waist. She opened her mouth to call out, but a hand covered her lips. She began to struggle wildly against her unseen assailant, but he forced her down on to the sleeping-bag. Just then his hand gently cupped the naked globe of her breast, and he whispered her name.

'Oh, Nick!' she protested, laughing and crying at the same time. 'You almost scared me to death!'

'I didn't mean to frighten you, little one,' he whispered, bending to touch his lips to hers. 'But I didn't want you to waken the Harrows.' His hands moved gently on her breasts and she sighed with pleasure. There was a soft, sweet tensing of the muscles in her loins.

'Did you want something?' she whispered coquettishly, covering his hands with hers.

He didn't answer, but she could feel his body stir against hers, and wordlessly she zipped open the sleeping-bag. At once he was beside her, his hot, naked skin pressed against her chilled body.

'I want you so much,' she whispered as her body began moving in an ancient rhythm against his.

'And I've never wanted any woman as I want you, Amanda,' he said as his hand moved between her warm thighs and to the damp, secret flesh beyond.

She would have cried out, unable to silence her passion, but his mouth covered hers as they gave themselves up to the silent, silken night.

CHAPTER NINE

LONG fingers of sunlight were just touching the sands when Amanda awoke. It was quiet outside the tent; apparently, no one was up and about at this early hour. Nick was gone from her side. Although he had teased her, he had kept his word and left in the still hours before dawn.

Amanda lay drowsing in the comfort of the warm sleeping-bag, thinking of all that had happened in the past hours. It was impossible to believe so much could have changed so quickly. She was happier than she could ever remember having been in her life, more alive, more fulfilled than she had dreamed possible. And yet a nagging doubt pursued her, the disquieting realisation that Nick had penetrated all her careful defences that had protected her from the world for so long. She turned on her side and pressed her face into the warm hollow where Nick had lain beside her. There was a faint, wonderful scent of him still there, and she breathed it in deeply, closing her eyes as she recalled the long hours of the night. It was impossible to think that this man would do anything to hurt her, she thought, brushing her doubts aside. Gradually she became aware of the whispered voices outside. There was no more time for worried introspection, and she dressed hurriedly and joined the others.

Shalal greeted her with a steaming mug of fragrant coffee to ward off the early morning chill.

'Good morning,' Charlie said cheerfully. 'How was your night?' Shalal threw him a glowering look and he

blushed with discomfort. 'I mean, did you have a good
night? Damn!' he muttered, turning beetroot-red. 'I'm
sorry, Amanda.'

Amanda eyed him levelly above her coffee-mug, trying
not to look at Nick, who was shaking with silent
laughter.

'That's all right, Charlie,' she said evenly. 'Thank you
for asking. Yes, I slept very well. Nick?'

He looked at her in surprise and then, as she stared
steadily at him, he nodded. 'Oh, yes, thanks, I was fine.
Very comfortable. There was plenty of room in the
supply tent.'

Shalal placed a platter of scrambled eggs and buttered
toast on the table. There was the ghost of a smile on her
face. 'Well, I'm glad everyone spent a pleasant night,'
she said. 'Now, can we get off this ridiculous subject?
Amanda, would you like some eggs?'

'Yes, please, Shalal. I can't remember ever being so
hungry before. It must be the desert air,' she added a
scant second too late, for Nick had already choked on his
coffee and Charlie's face was twitching uncontrollably.

'What shall we do this morning?' asked Shalal quickly,
staring sternly at the two men while Amanda wished
there was some way to hide herself. 'Perhaps you'd like
to see the ruins near here, Amanda?'

'Oh, I'd love to. Could we, Nick?'

'I don't see why not. We have the whole day ahead of
us.'

By the time the sun had begun to bake away all
memories of the night's chill they were piled in the jeep,
heading across the desert over a barely visible set of old,
packed tyre tracks. They reached the remains of the
ancient fort within half an hour, and Amanda was
immediately enchanted by its half-standing walls and
towers.

'I can almost picture the people who built this place,' she mused as they walked. 'All the knights riding off to battle, the Moors defending their land—it must have been exciting to have lived then.'

Shalal laughed. 'Only if you were a man, Amanda. For the women, life was nothing but drudgery. We were little more than possessions in those times.'

'Oh, I don't know if it was so bad,' said Charlie, winking broadly at Nick. 'A man could have himself a faithful wife and still enjoy the favours of all the pretty little things that came along as the spoils of war. What's wrong with that?'

Shalal linked her arm through his. 'We're too smart to let you men get away with that nonsense these days, aren't we, Amanda? Although some of you still try.'

'My former husband was like that,' Amanda said slowly as the Harrows walked on ahead. 'That's the kind of marriage he wanted, and he thought I was crazy when I objected.'

Nick's arm tightened protectively around her. 'Does it upset you to talk about him?'

'It was all so long ago that it's like talking about another lifetime. We weren't married very long, and I was awfully young and foolish, I guess.'

'He was the fool, not you, if he gave you up, little one.'

He touched his lips to her hair and she smiled up at him.

'I don't regret leaving him, Nick,' she explained. 'It's just that I should have known better. Todd had that kind of reputation on campus, and I knew it. It was foolish of me to think he'd be any different once we were married.'

'But if he loved you. . .'

'My father loved my mother,' she said softly, 'and that didn't stop him treating her the same way. You'd think

I'd have learned something, but. . .' her words trailed off into silence.

Gently Nick drew her closer to his side. 'You fell in love with the wrong man, little one. That's the only mistake you made.'

Amanda shook her head and sighed. 'You know, I'm not sure now that I really ever loved Todd. Oh, I thought I did, of course, but—well, I was so lonely on that big campus. And I'd spent so much time working towards a scholarship in high school that I never really learned how to make friends. And my mother. . .'

'Your mother must have been an unhappy woman, Amanda.'

'No, not really,' she said quickly. 'Just realistic. She tried to teach me to be independent. There's nothing wrong with that,' she added, almost defiantly.

Ahead, the Harrows waited for them in the shade cast by an overhanging parapet. Nick paused and pointed to the base of the fortress wall, where a slender green shoot wound its way through a crack and up the ancient stone surface.

'That vine has the kind of toughness and resilience it needs to survive in the desert, little one.' He bent and touched the curling dark green leaves. 'But it still needs the wall to lean on, to hold.'

Amanda looked at him and smiled stiffly. 'That's a lovely image, Nick. But the reality is that the wall doesn't need the vine, does it?'

'That's one of the things wrong with studying a science curriculum, Amanda,' he teased gently. 'If you'd spent more time reading poetry, you'd know that these stones need beauty to give them meaning.'

'But not to survive,' she insisted.

Nick clasped her hand in his and smiled. 'That depends on what you mean by survival, Amanda. Poets know that.'

She forced herself to return his smile as they came abreast of Charlie and Shalal. 'It's a good thing poets aren't building your irrigation project,' she said lightly, then she turned to Shalal. 'Are you ready for lunch yet?' she asked, before Nick could reply. 'Let me help you set out the food.'

The four of them ate lunch in the shadows cast by the old fort and then loaded the empty picnic hamper back into the jeep. The Harrows wanted to go back to the campsite to pick up some digging tools, and Nick suggested that he and Amanda spend part of the afternoon riding.

The horses trotted out into the desert, and Amanda marvelled at the tiny signs of life her city-dulled eyes had missed until Nick showed them to her, but even his best efforts failed to convince her that there were landmarks to follow in the vast expanse of white sand.

'It all looks the same,' she insisted, staring at the shifting dunes that surrounded them. 'I don't even know where our camp is.'

'Then you'd better behave yourself,' teased Nick. 'Otherwise I'll leave you here to find your own way back.'

'Don't joke about it, Nick. I really don't understand how you know where we are.'

'I've spent almost as much time out here as I have in Paris, little one. That was one of the benefits of being raised on two continents. By the time I was twelve I could as easily travel the desert as I could the Champs-Elysées.'

Amanda sighed wistfully. 'I'm still having trouble figuring out the New York subway system,' she admitted, and Nick laughed.

'I suspect I'd have difficulty with that, too,' he confessed. 'I'll tell you what, Amanda, we'll make a bargain. I'll guide you through the streets of Paris, if you'll help me solve the mystery of the subways. How does that sound?'

She stole a quick glance at him. His eyes were filled with goodnatured amusement, and she forced herself to smile.

'Sure,' she said casually, 'it's a deal.'

The hours passed quickly and by late afternoon the four of them were gathered at the campsite again, laughing and talking over coffee. There was a brief lull in the conversation and Shalal sighed deeply and cleared her throat.

'I hate to spoil things, you two, but Charlie and I have to return to the construction site at Marakef tomorrow. Are you going with us?'

'I'm afraid we'll have to,' answered Nick, 'although I wish we could stay out here longer. But at least we've had a couple of days before we have to go back to the real world.'

There was a sudden droning noise in the distance, shattering the peaceful quiet.

'What on earth is that?' asked Shalal, looking upward and shielding her eyes from the sun.

'It sounds like a helicopter. Yes, there it is, just coming over that dune.' Nick got to his feet and pointed towards the distant machine. 'This isn't an area that gets much traffic of any kind. It's got to be bad news.' Even as he spoke, the 'copter began to descend, its whirling blades whipping the sand into a clouded frenzy. 'Stay here!' Nick shouted above the noise of its engines. 'I'll find out what they want.'

Even before he returned and she saw the look on his face, Amanda knew somehow that their idyll had ended. When Nick took her hands in his, she forced herself to smile at him.

'We have to go back, don't we?' she asked.

'I'm so sorry, Amanda, but something's come up. There's a banking deal I've been involved in for some time, and Gamal's sent word that a problem's developed. If I don't go back now, we might lose millions. Can you forgive me?'

'Of course,' she said crisply, neither her voice or her face betraying the despair she felt. 'Shall I go with you, or do you want me to go on to Marakef with Shalal and Charlie?'

'You certainly are something,' said Nick. He looked at her for a long moment. 'I thought you'd be upset by this disruption, but here you are, ready to get back to work.'

'Back to the real world,' she said brightly. 'Isn't that what you said?'

Nick nodded. 'That's what I said, little one. But I thought. . .never mind,' he said quickly. 'Actually, if you don't mind, it would be most helpful if you went with the Harrows. Phone me just as soon as you get back to town.'

'Right,' she said, and he bent and kissed her lingeringly.

'Good luck!' she called after him as he sprinted towards the helicopter. He turned and waved once, and then he was swallowed up by the noisy machine. Amanda watched as it lifted into the twilight sky like a giant insect, until it was barely a pinpoint of light, then it disappeared from view.

She was quiet and subdued after Nick's departure. Even Charlie's gruff jokes fell flat on her ears. When Shalal suggested going to bed early so they could get up at dawn to break camp, Amanda readily agreed, eager to leave this place that now seemed barren and empty.

The next morning, in the chill of first light, they tied the horses to the back of the jeep and travelled slowly

towards Marakef. It turned out to be the kind of place
she had anticipated: stark, isolated, swarming with
workers and equipment. Charlie went to work immediately, aided by Shalal, and Amanda spent the day
conferring with field engineers and the crew chief. The
Harrows were leaving in two days, driving back to the
city over the old truck route, and she spent half the last
night working, compiling notes and checking reports, so
that she would be ready to go with them.

The return trip to the city was a long one, over a hot,
dusty road that was little more than a rough cut in the
desert sand. It took hours longer than the flight she had
made with Nick, but Amanda was tired and strangely
depressed, and she dozed fitfully most of the way.
Everything that had happened in the past few days
seemed somehow unreal and fragmented without Nick's
presence. When at last the Harrows dropped her off at
her hotel, so she could shower and change her clothes,
she felt as if she were slowly awakening from a deep
sleep.

CHAPTER TEN

HELEN greeted her with cheerful exuberance, a stack of mail, and a memo from the New York office.

'It's from Tim Pauling,' she explained, handing the slip of paper to Amanda. 'He called yesterday and said to tell you it was urgent, that he wanted to hear from you the minute you got in, no matter what the hour, New York time.' A mischievous grin lit her face. 'So I placed the call when you came through the door, A.S. The overseas lines are busy, but if it goes through soon we'll wake the dear man from a sound sleep.'

Amanda laughed as she dropped her mail on the desk. 'You really are terrible, you know that?'

'Just efficient, boss, just following orders,' her secretary said with artful innocence. 'So, how was your little jaunt with the Sheikh? That must have been some trip, hmm? I mean, just you and that gorgeous man, alone out under the desert stars. . .' She sighed and batted her eyelashes dramatically. 'Care to tell me about it?'

A faint blush spread over Amanda's cheeks and she swivelled her chair away from Helen's amused grin. 'There's nothing to tell,' she said calmly. 'But I would like you to start typing up some notes I made at Marakef. Could you start on them right away?'

'Sure, A.S., no problem.'

As soon as the door closed behind Helen, Amanda glanced at the telephone. She had promised to call Nick immediately, and the need to hear his familiar voice was almost overwhelming. But the sense of dreamlike unreality was still with her, the feeling that what had happened

between them was suspended in time and space, isolated
forever like a fragile flower in a Victorian paperweight.
As if summoned by her hesitant hand, the phone rang
just as her fingers touched it. Eagerly she snatched it up
in mid-ring, but it was Helen's voice that greeted her.

'I've got Tim on line one, A.S. The connection is really
rotten, but he says to go ahead anyway.'

There was a sibilant hiss of static on the overseas line,
then Amanda heard Tim's faint, tinny voice. She pressed
the receiver closer to her ear.

'Tim? I just got your message. What's up? Is
something wrong?'

'Damned right, Sutton,' he snapped. 'I'll get right to
it, before we lose this line completely. Remember that
project in California we bid on? The one in Rio Alto?
Well, we got it, a couple of weeks ago.'

'That's great, Tim. What's the problem, then?'

A snarl of static made Amanda wince, and then Tim's
voice drifted back again. '. . .losing the whole thing. I
wouldn't call it a problem, kid—it's more like a disaster!'

Amanda shook her head in frustration and shifted the
phone to her other ear. 'I couldn't hear what you said,'
she shouted. 'What are you losing?'

'The whole damned project, Sutton. I don't know what
that stupid Jensen did to blow the deal, but the Rio Alto
planning council is threatening to scrap the whole works.'

Another blast of incomprehensible sound came
through the receiver. 'Tim, this connection. . .'

'It's lousy, I know. I said, Sutton, you have to fly
home as soon as possible. I don't know if we can pull this
thing out of the fire, but we're damned well going to try.'

'Me? You want me to fly home? Why?'

Tim cursed vividly. 'This rotten phone!' he moaned
angrily. 'That's what I've been telling you, kid. They
won't deal with Jensen any more, and we've got to get

somebody out there, fast. I can't get away; I'm up to my teeth in a tough deal in New York. This Rio Alto thing isn't enormous, but it's vital for the West Coast operation, and it's kind of a scaled-down version of the job you're on now. That Marakef thing is going smoothly, isn't it?'

'Yes, but——'

'So that makes you the person I've got with the right kind of experience to handle this.'

Amanda drew in her breath as more interference garbled Tim's words. To be asked to take over a project, an important project, after an older, more experienced consultant had failed was the opportunity of a lifetime. And yet all she could think of was that it meant leaving Nick.

'I can't pull out of here so suddenly,' she protested. 'You have to give me some time. A few weeks. . .'

'The hard part's done, right? I can send Jensen to take your place.'

'But I can't leave yet, Tim!'

'Look, Sutton, don't get cute with me. A few months ago you were breathing down everybody's neck here, all hot and eager to move up the corporate ladder. Well, this is the first big step. Are you ready for it or not?'

'Yes, of course I am,' Amanda said quickly. 'But——'

'If you turn this down, kid, the door is closed, you know that. Anyway, if it makes you feel any happier, there's a rise and a promotion in it for you. You're a full consultant now. How does that sound?'

'Is sounds wonderful. It's just that I need more time. . .'

'I can't hear you, kid!' Tim shouted. 'Just get your tail on the first plane out tomorrow. Tell ben Saad I'll call him after I work out some details with Jensen. And by the way, Sutton,' he added gruffly, 'congratulations.'

Stunned, Amanda hung up the phone and waited for the heady exhilaration she knew she should be feeling, but there was nothing but numbness within her. Slowly she rose from her chair and walked to the window, gazing out at the silhouette of the city. She raised her eyes to the hills beyond, until the white house and its surrounding cypress trees came into view, almost seeming to float in the shimmering heat waves of the early afternoon sun. The sound of the door opening startled her. Helen stood framed in the doorway, peering through an enormous bouquet of yellow roses, a smug smile on her face.

'So the trip was strictly business, hmm?' She marched across the room and set the flowers down on the desk. 'From the Sheikh,' she said. 'That man really thinks of everything; they even came in this gorgeous vase. By the way, he called, while you were on the phone with Tim.'

'The Sheikh?' echoed Amanda, staring at the spectacular roses.

'Of course, the Sheikh, A.S., who else? He said you're to meet him at L'Epicure at one-thirty for lunch.' Helen started towards the door, then paused. 'And one last thing, boss—New York sent us some updated shipping schedules while you were away. Some pipe is going to arrive two weeks early, but four master valves will be a month late, so it looks like you're going to have to reschedule a couple of things or there'll be a mess.' She looked at Amanda questioningly. 'Is everything OK, A.S.? Did our leader in New York give you a hard time?'

Amanda looked up and shook her head. 'No, no, everything is fine. Just get those shipping updates together for me, will you?'

She sat staring at the flowers, knowing Nick must be waiting to hear from her, wondering what to say to him, how to tell him about Tim's call. How would he react? she wondered. Would he ask her to stay with him? And if he did, what then? She took one of the roses from the vase and inhaled its delicate perfume, remembering the desert wildflowers and the hours she had spent in Nick's arms. She loved him, she knew that without question. In spite of all her plans, all her carefully wrought defences, she loved him in a way she had never dreamed she could love anyone. With a suddenness that brought a tremor to her fingers she recalled his hands on her body, his mouth on hers, and all at once she knew there was really no need to ask him if he wanted her to stay in Morocco. She already knew the answer, as surely as she knew that she had no desire to leave him. For the first time since they had parted in the desert, Amanda felt a dizzying rush of joy. With a recklessness that outraged the part of herself that was quietly clucking at such illogical foolishness, she made her decision and reached for the phone to call Tim—and almost laughed aloud as she thought of how stunned he would be when she told him she was staying in Morocco.

'Hello? Amanda, is that you?'

'Nick!' she said with delight. 'I just picked up the phone to make a call. I didn't expect to hear your voice.'

He laughed softly. 'I just this second dialled your number, little one. It must be extra-sensory perception. I just had to hear your voice, Amanda, to touch you somehow, to make sure it wasn't a dream, even if it has to be over a telephone line.'

'I was going to call you,' she said quickly, 'but I only just got in, and there was a message to call Tim, in New York.'

'And you called him first?' he teased gently. 'Don't tell me he's more important to you than I am!'

'He'd left word that it was urgent, Nick, and it was. Tim said——'

'Amanda,' Nick murmured softly, 'I didn't call you to

talk business. Did you get the roses?'

'Yes,' she whispered, reaching out to touch the beautiful flowers, 'and they're lovely. Thank you.'

'You're welcome. You can thank me properly later.'

She blushed at the soft, suggestive caress of his voice. 'Don't you think that might upset the other people at the restaurant?'

He sighed and cleared his throat. 'It's a tempting idea, little one, but it'll have to wait. I'm going to have to cancel our luncheon appointment. When I called before, I thought we'd made some progress here, but it hasn't worked out. I'm sorry.'

'I am, too,' she said slowly. 'There's something we have to talk about.'

'I've been tied up with this Swiss banker since yesterday,' Nick continued, as if she hadn't spoken, 'and I still haven't nailed down the loan we need. Just a second, Amanda.' There was the murmur of voices in the background, and when he spoke again his voice was low and hurried. 'Little one, I'm going to have to cut this short. My work's closing in on me here.'

'Nick,' she said quickly, eager to share the happiness of her news with him, 'just give me a minute. I have to tell you about my talk with Tim.'

'You can tell me about it tonight, Amanda,' he said. 'I promise,' he added, chuckling softly, 'I'll give you an entire thirty seconds to talk business.'

'This isn't something to joke about, Nick,' she said, a slight note of irritation creeping into her voice. 'It's important.'

'I'm sure it is,' he said, as patiently as if she were a small child interrupting an adult conversation. 'But it can wait until tonight. I'll pick you up at your hotel at seven.'

She thought of the schedules that needed completion and frowned. 'That's too early. I have some work to do here at the office, and I won't be done by then.'

'Amanda,' he said gently, 'the only thing you have to do is think about me and tonight.' His voice dropped to a teasing whisper. 'I'll have to think of some way to keep your mind off your job and on me, where it belongs.'

She drew a deep breath. 'Don't make fun of me, Nick. My work is important to me.'

'We can argue about that tonight, little one, if you insist, although I'll bet I can change your mind. I'll see you at seven sharp.'

'Nick. . .'

'Seven o'clock, Amanda,' he repeated. 'I'm taking you to a very special place for dinner. You're going to love it.'

She stared at the silent telephone for a second, then slammed it down. One weekend together, she thought, and already he'd begun to arrange her life to suit his! It was as if he thought she was some malleable substance that could be shaped and moulded to accommodate him, as if her needs were not as important as his.

Absently she swivelled her chair until she was facing the window. It was senseless to be so annoyed at Nick, she reminded herself. After all, hadn't she already decided to change her life to fit his, even though he didn't know it yet? Once she turned down the promotion, that would be the end of her career at Olsen & Tibbs. Suppose they fired her as soon as they knew she didn't want the assignment in the States? She thought of the money in her small savings account, wondering if it would last until she found another job. Were there other companies here that would hire a woman engineer? Probably not, she admitted to herself. If she was a rarity in the States, she was almost an oddity here in this strange place with its male-dominated society. There were always openings for English-speaking secretaries in the larger firms, but she winced at the thought of setting

aside all her technical training, all her skills, to pound
away at a typewriter. And she didn't even do that very
well, she thought ruefully. Yet a job would have to be her
first priority, unless she wanted to let Nick. . .never! she
thought fiercely. No matter what else she gave up, she'd
never depend on him for that kind of help.

She took a deep breath and turned back to her desk,
reminding herself that all that mattered was Nick. She
wanted to stay here, to stay with him. Nothing was more
important than their need to be together. She would stay
in Morocco, she would get a job, and she would be with
Nick. A sudden picture of herself, sitting in her hotel
room waiting patiently for him to call, flashed into her
mind. What would she do the nights, the weekends, that
he didn't? she wondered. And what if, eventually, he
didn't call at all? He wanted her now, she knew that, but
would it last? And for how long? She put her hands over
her eyes, as if by pressing lightly on her eyelids she could
drive out such harsh, ugly thoughts, but the truth was
that these were realities that had to be considered. The
simple, happy decision she had made so easily only
minutes earlier suddenly seemed as complex as a problem
in advanced physics. Her hand, poised seconds before to
pick up the phone and call Tim, hesitated, then moved to
the intercom instead.

Amanda spent the remaining afternoon hours poring
over the new shipping schedules, telling herself she
would call Tim when she had finished. But at five
o'clock, with the schedules still not completed and the
call still unmade, she cleared off her desk and left the
office. A cooling breeze had sprung up, carrying with it
the faint, scented promise of rain, and her footsteps
slowed in grateful response to its pleasant touch. She
walked slowly down the wide boulevard, savouring its
sights and sounds, unable to picture herself back on the

crowded, hectic streets of New York. As she passed the office of Air Morocco, she averted her eyes guiltily, uncomfortable with the knowledge that Tim expected her to leave the next day, trying to imagine what Nick would say when she told him what had happened, what she had given up so she could remain here with him. Her initial elation had given way to an uneasy feeling of discomfort, a heavy awareness that it was almost as if he held her future in his hands. She thought of how totally she was turning herself over to him, how completely she had retreated from everything she believed in, how clouded the future seemed, and something seemed to constrict within her chest and throat.

She began to walk more quickly, urging herself to ignore the doubts and fears that were skittering through her thoughts like phantom figures in a mirage. With a weary sigh she reached the last, long block before her hotel. She glanced at her watch and reminded herself that in just an hour and a half Nick would be with her. Nothing would matter once she was safely within the warming shelter of his arms. Caught up in her own world, she stepped off the kerb and a horn blared directly in front of her. Startled, she looked up just as a red Ferrari raced down the boulevard and braked to a stop in front of a small hotel only half a block away. Amanda stood still, oblivious to the angry shouts of a cab driver as he swerved to avoid her. The noise of the traffic faded to a meaningless roar as she watched, transfixed, as a tall man leaped from the Ferrari and hurried around to its other side. He pulled open the door and a young woman slid gracefully from the low-slung seat. She looked up into the man's face, tossed back her dark hair, and laughed. As they walked into the hotel, she took his arm and he smiled down at her.

It was Nick.

CHAPTER ELEVEN

'TRUST me,' he had said. 'I'll never hurt you,' he had promised. Nick's whispered words seemed to reverberate all around her. Somehow she managed to reach the safety of her hotel and the seclusion of her room. There was a tight, knotted feeling behind her eyes, as if she was going to cry, yet no tears came. She sat down carefully on the edge of the bed, as if any sudden movement might make her shatter into a thousand pieces. Over and over she told herself that there must be a perfectly rational explanation for what she had seen, but the more she replayed the scene she had witnessed, the more intimate it became.

As the early evening shadows lengthened into darkness, Amanda rose from the bed and went through the motions of changing her clothes, although she paid scant attention to the dress she pulled from the closet. A glance in the mirror was far from reassuring: her blue eyes had a clouded, dull look to them, and there were shadows beneath them, like ashen smudges against the honeyed tan of her skin. By quarter to seven she felt as if she'd worn a pathway in the nubby tweed carpet, and she snatched up a sweater and went down to the lobby.

A light rain began just as she reached the street, and she turned her face up towards the sky, closing her eyes wearily. A horn beeped once; she looked down the circular driveway just as the red Ferrari pulled in towards her. Nick grinned as she opened the door and slid into the car.

'You looked like a rain goddess standing out there,' he

told her, pulling out into the sparse traffic. He reached across the console and took her hand in his. 'I've missed you, Amanda,' he added softly, raising her fingers to his lips. 'It's been a long three days.'

'Has it?' she asked, hating the stilted sound of her own voice. 'I suppose it has,' she added quickly, 'but I've been terribly busy, first at Marakef and then at the office.'

Nick looked over at her. 'Are you all right? You sound edgy.'

'I'm fine, Nick. Just a little tired.'

'And a little wet,' he laughed, touching her damp hair. 'But you can dry out when we get to the inn. They'll have a fire laid out, waiting for us, and a bottle of burgundy.' He waited for her to answer, but she was staring straight ahead, watching the rain. 'You're going to love this place, Amanda. It's very special to me.'

'Is it far?'

He shook his head. 'No, not at all. It's just up the coast a few miles. Amanda,' he queried hesitantly, 'what is it? You're very quiet this evening.'

'I told you,' she said evenly, 'I'm tired, that's all.'

Nick smiled and reached for her hand. 'Not too tired, I hope. I spent the day counting the hours until we'd be together.'

She moved her hand away from his and placed it in her lap. 'Did you? I thought you'd have been too busy to think of anything but your banker. How did it go, by he way? Did you finally get what you wanted?'

He nodded and shifted down as the car began climbing a narrow road breasting the sea. 'I got the loan, or at least the promise of one. And that reminds me, little one—I promised you thirty seconds to tell me what was so important about Tim's call, remember? Why don't you tell me about it now?' He smiled at her and added softly,

'I'd rather not waste time on business once we get to the inn.'

'I'll wait,' Amanda said stiffly, as the car pulled into a hidden driveway and came to a stop behind a two-storey, slate-roofed building. 'What is this place, Nick? I thought you said it was an inn.'

'It is, Amanda. It's run by an old couple from Normandy.' He took her arm and led her to a door half concealed in a tangle of thick ivy that grew up walls of worn red brick. 'There's a private staircase to the upper floor,' he explained when she hesitated. 'It's all right, little one, Claudine and Paul know we're coming.'

The winding staircase within finally opened on to a small landing. Nick pushed open a heavy oak door and she stepped into a charming, heavily beamed room. Its focal point was an enormous old brick fireplace, almost large enough to stand in. Off through a partially opened door she could see a massive spindle bed.

'I thought you said we were going to have dinner here,' she said, turning away from the open doorway.

'And so we are,' he whispered, coming up behind her and putting his hands lightly on her shoulders. 'Right here, in front of the fireplace.'

Deftly Amanda moved away from the touch of his hands, towards the centre of the room. 'I suppose you've been here many times,' she said tonelessly.

Nick nodded casually. 'Yes, of course. We sometimes have clients who prefer the privacy of this suite, and occasionally we hold private meetings here.'

'Business meetings?' she asked, her eyes flicking towards the bedroom door.

He walked over to her and eased the sweater from her shoulders. 'I've never brought a woman here, Amanda, if that's what you're asking.'

'But there have been women in your life, haven't there?'

'None that ever mattered,' he said gently, turning her to face him and running his finger over her lips. 'Don't you think we're wasting a lot of precious time, little one? You haven't even kissed me hello.' He bent his head and touched his mouth softly to hers and an anticipatory tingle ran through her. She felt herself leaning into the hard warmth of his embrace, and she took a deep breath and moved back from his encircling arms.

'I'm a little chilled, Nick. Didn't you promise me some wine and a fire?'

A confused expression clouded his eyes for a second, then his hands dropped to his sides. 'Yes, of course. Perhaps that's what we both need.' She watched silently as he knelt and struck a match to the kindling in the old fireplace. After the flames danced up and began to lick at the logs, he took a bottle of wine from a cherrywood sideboard and filled two exquisite gold-rimmed glasses with the dark burgundy liquid. 'Paul chose a fine vintage,' he said, handing her one of the glasses, 'but it's not the equal of this crystal. I've been trying to persuade him to sell me this old set for years. Beautiful, isn't it?'

'You're quite a collector, aren't you, Nick?' she asked, sipping tentatively at the wine. 'Painting, sculpture, racing trophies, antiques. . .'

'You make it sound like an accusation, Amanda! I told you, I enjoy collecting lovely things. Is there something wrong with that?'

'I don't know,' she said slowly. 'It all depends, I guess. I remember a man back home who collected butterflies. I asked him once when his collection would be complete, and he said it never would, that after he'd added a new butterfly to his collection, he lost interest in it and started searching for the next one.'

There was an uncomfortable silence, then Nick put down his glass and walked towards her. 'Will you please tell me what's going on?' he asked. 'It seems to me we've been talking in riddles all evening.'

The words she had planned to say caught in her throat. 'I'm sorry,' she sighed. 'I told you I was tired. You must be, too. Didn't you say you were tied up in meetings all day?'

The taut lines in his face relaxed and he ran his hand through his dark hair. 'From early morning until just before I got to your hotel,' he said, smiling at her, 'I spent the entire day trying to shake some money out of that damned banker. It's impossible to please those people.'

'A Swiss banker, you said, didn't you?' Amanda forced her eyes to meet his. 'I've never met one, but I always picture grey flannel and pinstripes.'

'That's the uniform most of them wear,' laughed Nick, 'but no matter what they look like, they all have one thing in common: they hate to part with money. You'd be amazed at what you have to do before they give you anything in return.'

'It must have been rough,' she said, forcing herself to return his smile.

'It was, little one, but I'm used to it.'

'Just part of the job,' she commented, as he moved closer to her. 'Isn't that right?'

'Right,' he said softly, running his hands up her arms.

'Like me?' she asked, trying to ignore the touch of his fingers against her skin. 'After all, I was part of the job.'

'You were a bonus,' he whispered throatily, pulling her into his arms.

She felt the warmth of his breath against her cheek and saw the deepening blue in his eyes as his arms tightened around her. For a brief second she almost gave in to the desire to wrap her arms around his neck and raise her mouth to his, then with an enormous effort she looked away from his face, back towards the bedroom door.

'I saw you today,' she said suddenly, before she could think, shocked at the sound of her own words. 'Near my hotel, at a little past five.'

'Did you?' he asked, a frown creasing his forehead.

'Oh, yes,' she said, her eyes focusing on his. 'You were going into the Hotel Columbine.'

'The Columbine. . .of course, Amanda. We went there for cocktails, after we'd finished negotiations.'

'For cocktails,' she repeated. 'You and the Swiss banker?'

'Yes,' Nick said slowly, 'me and. . .' A smile touched his lips and he shook his head. 'Is that what this is all about? It is, isn't it? You saw me with Greta and you thought. . .Amanda, love, that was the banker you saw me with!'

'There's an old American joke like that,' she said carefully. 'You're supposed to say. "That was no lady, that was my banker". Then everybody is supposed to laugh.'

'Amanda,' he said patiently, 'that's precisely who she was. Why didn't you simply ask me?'

'Why didn't you simply tell me?'

'You didn't ask, Amanda,' he said in the same patient tone, 'and it never occurred to me that it would matter to you.'

She backed away from him and smiled coolly. 'You mean it never occurred to you that I'd find out, don't you, Nick?'

'This is ridiculous,' he said firmly. 'A little jealousy is flattering, but being called a liar isn't.'

A faint, warning bell seemed to sound in her head, and she hesitated. 'I. . .I didn't call you a liar,' she said quickly, and the look on his face softened.

'I'm glad to hear it, little one,' he said, and smiled at her. 'Now, is that all settled?' She didn't answer, and he tilted her chin up. 'I don't want anything special to spoil tonight,' he told her softly. 'I have something special in mind.'

'Nick,' she said hurriedly, 'there's something else.' She took a deep breath and spoke before he could stop her. 'That call from Tim. . .he wants me to fly back to New York. The company's given me a promotion, and an assignment in the States.'

'I see,' he said, his expression unchanging. 'And what did you tell him?'

'Nothing,' she stammered. 'I. . .I didn't say anything.'

'You should have told him you weren't going,' he said, and something that had been trembling within her seemed to take wing and soar free. 'You can't leave me— you know that, don't you?' His hands slipped to her shoulders and he smiled at her. 'Is that what you had to talk to me about?' he asked, and she nodded. 'Well then, I was right, wasn't I? All it took was thirty seconds to solve that problem.' His arms moved around her and she sighed and leaned against him. 'I want you right here with me, where you belong, little one,' he whispered. 'You know that, don't you?' She looked up at him and he bent and kissed her lingeringly. 'I told you tonight was going to be special, Amanda. Don't you want to know why?' She blushed and closed her eyes, and he laughed softly. 'That's not exactly what I meant, love,' he said, kissing the tip of her nose. 'We're going to Paris next week, you and I.'

Amanda drew back in his arms and stared at him in surprise. 'Paris?' she repeated.

'That's right,' he said triumphantly, grinning at her. 'And I won't accept any excuses about all the work you have to do, so while I'm in Zurich on Thursday and Friday, finish up everything on your desk.'

'I don't understand, Nick. What are you talking about?'

'I have to go to Zurich tomorrow, Amanda. This loan we're negotiating is quite large, and Girard et Fils won't give final approval until after I've met with their Board of Directors. And so, tomorrow. . .'

She felt as if an icy hand had reached out and touched her, and she shivered in spite of the heat from the blazing fire. 'Let me guess,' she said, her voice barely a whisper. 'You're going to fly to Zurich, and your. . .your banker is going with you. Is that right?'

'I promise, I'll be back in two days, Amanda, maybe less.'

'Why should you rush back?' she asked brightly, turning away from him, praying he couldn't see the pain in her eyes. 'You just said we're not going to Paris until next week.'

Nick took her by the shoulders and forced her to face him. 'I want to spend the weekend with you,' he said quietly.

'You mean you'll give up two days in Zurich just for me? I'm flattered, really!'

'Amanda, stop this nonsense,' he snapped angrily. 'I have a job to do, nothing more.'

'I'll bet you do,' she answered evenly. 'Do you have our weekend all planned, too? Are you going to take me out to an oasis again? Or will it be somewhere closer to home?'

'We can go anywhere, do anything you like, Amanda. The only thing I want is for us to be together,' he said, his voice softening as he looked at her. 'I keep remembering that night in El Quamar and how beautiful you were in that caftan. I want to buy you something like that to take to Paris with us.'

'Of course,' she said politely, although she wanted to strike out at him to ease the anguish building within her. 'You want to outfit me properly.' She glanced down at the simple cotton dress she was wearing and a brittle smile touched her lips. 'I really don't look right for Paris, or for Zurich, for that matter, do I?'

Nick's eyes flashed with anger. 'What on earth is the matter with you, Amanda? The trip to Zurich is business—I told you that. I won't have time for anything else, or I'd have asked you to come with me.'

'But you'll have time for me in Paris, I suppose.'

'Paris will be special, Amanda. It will be just for us.'

'And Zurich is just for you,' she snapped. 'Isn't that right?'

His fingers bit into her shoulders and he shook her. 'Dammit, stop this right now! I don't know what the hell's got into you, Amanda, but you're not making any sense. There are some things I simply must do.'

'Of course there are,' she answered, almost gently, an undercurrent of irony in her words. 'I'll just have to learn to accept that, won't I? Why don't you tell me what happens after Paris, though? You have everything else all planned; surely you must have arranged that, too.'

His face was white with anger. 'Are you worried about your damned independence again?' he growled. 'Don't worry; I have no intention of infringing upon it. If you want to keep your job, I won't stop you. Otherwise. . .'

'Otherwise you'll take care of me, I suppose. Is that what you were going to say? Well, I don't need taking care of,' she said, her voice rising and anger flaming in her cheeks. 'I can take care of myself very well, thank you. And I don't have a job, Nick, I have a career, and the next step up is waiting for me in New York.'

His hands tightened on her shoulders until she could feel the steely imprint of each finger. 'Have you gone crazy?' he demanded.

'Quite the contrary,' she said quickly. 'I've just put everything into perspective, that's all. I worked too hard to get where I am, and I have no intention of giving it up to become a. . .a collector's item. You should have consulted me first, before you made any plans for us. I wouldn't have gone to Paris with you, even if I weren't leaving tomorrow.'

'What in hell are you talking about, Amanda? You're not leaving, remember? We settled all that before.'

'You may have settled it,' she said coldly, 'but I certainly didn't. I'm going back to the States, Nick. I want that promotion.'

Nick shook his head and stared at her. 'I don't believe you,' he said after a moment. 'You can't just leave and pretend nothing has happened!'

'I'm not pretending anything. I simply realised that what we have isn't what I want.'

His eyes darkened until they were almost black. 'You're lying, Amanda,' he whispered. 'To me and to yourself. This isn't you.'

'Oh, but it is,' she said calmly, forcing her eyes to meet his. 'It's very much me, I assure you. We've had a pleasant few days together, Nick, let's not spoil them now.'

His fingers bit into her flesh for another few seconds. Then, slowly, the pressure eased and he released her and dropped his hands to his sides.

'They say some prisoners eventually feel unhappy anywhere but inside the walls of their cells,' he said. 'I suppose I can understand that. But you've gone a step further—you've built your own walls, your own prison, to hide in. I feel sorry for you, Amanda.'

'I don't need your pity,' she said quickly. 'I told you that once before.'

'It's the only thing I have left to offer,' said Nick, turning his back and walking out of the room.

CHAPTER TWELVE

NEW YORK was somehow different from how she remembered it. It seemed dirtier, less exciting, less attractive than before. But the impersonal energy of the place, the faceless crowds, the very noise and confusion of the city, were exactly what she needed. The hours of hurried, rushed packing in Morocco had mercifully left her with no time to think, but the seemingly endless flight home had been almost unbearable. She tried reading, napping, chatting briefly with the woman seated next to her, but in the end she gave up all attempts at diversion and stared blindly out into the bluish-white sky, trapped in a cocoon of unhappiness. At least, when she finally tumbled from the taxi into her apartment, she was too exhausted to think of anything except how desperately she needed some sleep.

When she arrived at the office the next day, Tim beamed at her and pumped her hand heartily.

'Sutton, it's good to see you! You did a pretty decent job for us over there, you know. All the reports I've seen have been great: the project's on schedule, and within cost guidelines.' He grinned at her and cleared his throat. 'You're OK, kid. I thought you'd need a day or two to recover from jet lag, but here you are, raring to go.'

'Thanks, Tim. I'm glad you're satisfied. And you're right, I am eager to get started. When do I leave for California?'

Tim patted her on the back and whistled noiselessly through his teeth. 'You know, you've almost changed my attitude about women, Sutton. In the old days, it was the guys, the young hotshots on their way up, who were always chomping at the bit. But you—well, if we had more like you, we'd really be cooking. I mean, I used to worry about broads. . .sorry, women,' he said quickly, reddening slightly, 'getting sidetracked by other things. You know, men, babies, that kind of thing. But you've got your eye on the top, haven't you?'

Amanda nodded and smiled slightly. 'Absolutely, Tim,' she said. 'I know exactly what I want.'

'Yeah, well, I guess right now you want the details on this new assignment, right? I've left some files on your desk, in your new office,' he added pointedly. 'Why don't you go through them, take a couple of hours to familiarise yourself with the data, and then we can talk over lunch.' He grinned slyly. 'No deli sandwiches at your desk today, kid—I've made a reservation at the Four Seasons. That way we can talk without interruption. Besides,' he added gruffly, 'I guess you deserve a little welcome home treat.'

Amanda spent the morning going through the records of the Rio Alto project. Gradually bits and pieces of the problem that had developed began to fall into place. Bill Jensen had gone into the sleeply little California town like a man on a mission, determined to score a big contract for the firm. He'd tried to charm the town council into enlarging and redesigning its plans, and when that hadn't worked, he'd simply tried to overwhelm them with facts and figures. Amanda remembered her small town beginnings; she knew that people in such places didn't take kindly to the pushy tactics of outsiders. It didn't take long to figure out that Bill Jensen had offended everybody involved. As if that weren't enough, a few simple calculations convinced her that the council's fairly simple, relatively inexpensive original proposal was basically sound and sensible. There was some damage to be undone, some fences to be mended, if the council was to be stopped from discarding the entire project or, worse still, awarding the contract to another firm. She made some notes while she read, and, by the time she and Tim had been seated at a table beside the handsome reflecting pool in the sweet restaurant, she had already begun to plan her approach to the Rio Alto situation. After they had ordered, she outlined some of her ideas to Tim.

'Sounds right on the money to me, kid,' he said, ignoring his salad and gazing hungrily at the oeufs à la russe on her plate. 'When will you be ready to leave for the West Coast?'

'I'll leave on Monday, Tim,' she told him. 'I just want to check some pipe specifications before I sketch out some final ideas, and I should be able to finish that over the weekend.'

He gave an exaggerated sigh of relief. 'Glad to hear it, Sutton. I told the boss you'd get a handle on this mess right away.' He pointed at her plate and added wistfully, 'You going to finish all that?'

Amanda smiled and shook her head. 'Actualy, I'm not really very hungry,' she said, pushing the plate towards him. 'You mean you managed to put in a good word about me upstairs? I can't believe I heard you right,' she teased, unable to resist the gentle dig.

Tim squirmed a bit in embarrassment. 'Well, what's fair is fair, kid, and I've got to admit you carried things off in Morocco. Matter of fact, I was a little worried about pulling you out of there so fast. But you didn't leave any loose ends behind, did you?'

'No,' she answered, looking away from him. 'No loose ends.'

'Good girl! You keep this up, and who knows what comes next?' He put down his fork and hiccupped

gently. 'Well, that's it for me. Unless you want
something with your coffee,' he added, stealing a quick
glance at a pastry cart laden with elaborate confections.

'No, thank you, Tim. I want to get back to the office,
but don't let me stop you. You can take your time and I'll
go on ahead.'

'That's OK, I'll pass—my wife has been after me to
lose some weight. See what a good influence you are,
Sutton?'

'Tim,' Amanda said lightly, 'let's not go overboard.
You're going to turn my head.'

'No kidding, Sutton, I mean it. This California thing
isn't a major project for us, we both know that, but the
West Coast branch needs a shot in the arm. If we can pull
this off, their balance sheet will be in the black. The big
boys upstairs would be mighty pleased. You'd rate a pat
on the back, at least.'

'I'd be satisfied with some time off,' she answered,
dropping her napkin on the table. 'I'm still trying to
adjust to New York time; after a few days on the coast, I
bet I won't know what day of the week it is.'

Tim signalled for the check and grinned at her. 'Tell
you what, Sutton—pull this one out of the fire for us and
you can take some time off, say a week or ten days. Take
yourself a little vacation on Olsen & Tibbs.' He handed
the waiter his American Express card and looked across
the table at her. 'You come from somewhere near Los
Angeles, don't you? Why not go home and show 'em
what a winner looks like?'

'I don't think so,' she said, remembering all too clearly
how uncomfortable her last visit home had been, how
little she and her mother had said to each other. 'It's
a busy time of year for my mother's shop,' she added
quickly, before he could say anything. 'But San Francisco
is a great city for a vacation, and I haven't been there

since I was a child.'

'Consider it done, kid. You've earned it.'

Amanda spent the rest of the day at her desk, comparing notes and checking figures. By the time she left for California, her briefcase was bulging with notes she had compiled over the weekend.

A somewhat subdued Bill Jensen met her at the San Francisco airport.

'The office suggested I drive you to Rio Alto,' he mumbled, 'so I can brief you on the way and introduce you to the city council manager.'

'You don't have to do that, Bill,' she said uncomfortably. 'I can manage on my own.'

He gave her a crooked grin. 'I'm sure you can,' he said, tossing her suitcase into the back seat of his car, 'but those are my orders. Anyway, I want you to know I don't resent your being here, Amanda. I screwed it up and I know it.'

'Come on, Bill, it isn't that bad. You did all the groundwork, after all. If I can sell them on our proposal, it will be because you made it easy for me.'

Jensen smiled at her. 'Nice try, Amanda, but no sale. We both know you're the new miracle worker for Olsen & Tibbs. And I really do wish you well. The way things are going, I might just be working for you one of these days. The scuttlebutt around here is that you're going to be Olsen & Tibbs' first woman vice-president. Anyway, it can't hurt to have you remember old Bill Jensen kindly, now can it?'

They both laughed, but his words remained with her. It was true, she thought, as they drove into the dusty central California countryside, her career was moving ahead. She knew it, they all knew it—and yet there was no heady feeling of excitement, no rush of pride within her. She urged herself to remember that she'd done the right thing, made the only decision possible, that this feeling of emptiness would pass once she got involved in the new assignment. But a peculiar sense of unreality persisted; even as she met the Rio Alto town manager and went over figures and plans with him, a part of her remained detached and separate. She felt as if she were standing in the wings of a theatre, watching herself perform. At least, she assured herself, she performed well.

The manager was a big, middle-aged man who looked as if he would rather be out riding a tractor than sitting behind a desk. At first he seemed a bit uncomfortable and wary of her, but as she pointed out the strengths in the original proposal and assured him that the few minor changes she had suggested were inexpensive and more efficient, he began to relax. She fell easily into the comfortable, small town behaviour she had grown up with, avoiding the high-tech jargon that might scare him off. By the close of the day they were on a first-name basis, and halfway through the next Amanda knew she had won him over. Presenting her plans to the assembled council that evening was only a matter of polite formality. When she phoned Tim to report that the deal was closed, he seemed more impressed than she was.

'You've got the touch, kid, a knack for sitting down and talking to people. As for Jensen. . .can you believe he's already messing things up in Morocco?'

'I don't understand, Tim. I thought the project there was going along smoothly.'

Tim's exasperated cluck carried clearly over the long-distance line. 'Not your baby at Marakef, Sutton, that's OK. But ben Saad is involved with something new, some kind of plant in another part of the country. They're just working out the financing; they suggested we might be interested in a bid on some of the construction. Anyway,

Jensen got off the plane and sat in on a meeting with Nick's people, and he said something out of left field about costs that scared hell out of the rep from the Sheikh's Swiss bank.'

'Girard et Fils?'

'That's it, kid. So now everybody is backing off, including this broad from the bank. Boy, you ladies are everywhere, aren't you?' he laughed. 'Banking, engineering—the only thing we have left is the locker room, and that's going, too.'

'But Nick. . .surely the Sheikh can reassure her. . .the banker. . .that Jensen's over-estimating costs,' Amanda said slowly.

'Not very likely, Sutton. Nobody's even seen the guy since he and Abdul Gamal went to Zurich with the lady last week. He's supposed to be in some cross-country racing thing in Africa. Kenya, I think.' Tim laughed again. 'Even the ever diplomatic old Gamal is ticked off. Says his boss has never been out of touch like this before. Anyway, we'll work it out. Unless you want to go back over there, kid?'

'No,' she said quickly. 'I'm not going back, Tim. You promised me a vacation, remember?'

'Only kidding, Sutton, only kidding. We're lining up something else for you, anyway. Enjoy San Francisco, kid.'

Amanda hung up the phone and walked to the window of her hotel room. The night sky was like a black field shot through with silver stars, but none seemed as bright as those over the Moroccan desert. She took several deep breaths, trying to still the erratic thudding of her heart. So Abdul Gamal had gone along on the trip to Zurich; it had indeed been business. Perhaps she should have listened to Nick, believed him. . . She shook her head angrily as if to clear it of such useless nonsense. What

would it have mattered, after all? He was off somewhere,
even now, collecting racing trophies, no doubt, and he
would probably add another pretty face while he was at
it. All he had offered her, all he had been willing to
commit himself to, was a weekend in the desert, a week
in Paris, an occasional sharing of his life, for which she
had been expected to give up everything. She closed her
eyes to the cold brilliance of the night sky and turned
away from the window.

'Depend only upon yourself, Amanda,' she whispered
in the stillness of the impersonal, plastic hotel room.
'That's the only way.'

As she undressed, she suddenly realised with surprise
that she hadn't even asked Tim about the new assignment he had mentioned. Well, of course not, she
thought. She was exhausted, after all. It was under-
standable. Deliberately, she concentrated on her new
title, her rise, her new office, until at last sleep overtook
her. And yet, when she finally fell into deep slumber, she
dreamed of none of those things. She dreamed only of
Nick.

CHAPTER THIRTEEN

BILL JENSEN had recommended a hotel in the heart of San Francisco, and it was everything he had promised: intimate, charming, almost Continental in atmosphere. Amanda's bedroom had a small sitting-room attached to it, and in the morning she sat at a tiny white wrought-iron table beside a window looking out on a flower-filled garden, sipping her coffee and planning her day's activities. And the city itself was wonderful, a picture-perfect series of breathtaking water views, tumbling hills, and charming architecture. She crammed the first day with all the things her guide book suggested, and that meant riding the cable cars, strolling through Chinatown, even taking a ferry out to the hulking grey mass that was Alcatraz Island and imagining the days when the damp stone walls contained hundreds of milling prisoners.

But at night, when the city by the bay blazed with lights and the Golden Gate Bridge gleamed like a series of bright jewels against the blackness of the water, Amanda's steps faltered. By night, the city seemed filled with couples. There seemed to be lovers strolling hand in hand everywhere she turned, and she fled back to the security of her sitting-room, where she watched old movies on the flickering television set until, yawning with weariness, she tumbled into bed.

When she awoke the next morning, a milky fog lay moistly against the window. She was amazed at how it obliterated everything outside, how even the sounds from the street seemed muffled. She had planned a walk through Golden Gate Park to the Japanese Tea House, but it would have to wait. Idly she flipped through her guide book. There was a museum she wanted to see, but she shuddered at the thought of driving anywhere in her rented car. The sharply inclined streets were challenge enough; to try and navigate them in such a heavy fog was madness.

Amanda reached out and flicked on the television set, as much for the noise as anything else, watching without interest while a smiling housewife sang the praises of her laundry detergent. The screen flickered and suddenly the airline commercial Helen had joked about so long ago flashed before her, while a voice smooth as silk began the familiar litany: 'Casablanca, Morocco. . .' She banged her fist on the on-off button and the screen went dark.

Vacations weren't all they were touted as being, she thought. At least work, hard work kept you from brooding. 'Never apologise for working hard,' her mother always said. What she hadn't added was that working hard at something was the only way to fill the vacuum that seemed to be suddenly lurking around the edges of her life.

She wondered what would happen if she phoned Tim and told him she was ready to go back to work. He'd probably nominate her for a medal, she thought grimly. It occurred to her that she could cut her stay short and fly home to New York, to her apartment, but the prospect of rattling around in those impersonally furnished three rooms was not enticing. Home, after all, was Santa Margarita, the little town she had grown up in, the kids she had known in school, the tiny upstairs bedroom overlooking a grassy backgarden filled with the heady, sweet smell of honeysuckle from the thick vines that grew rampant over the old stone wall at the back of the house. She smiled wistfully, remembering how many times she had sat in the shade of those stones, smelling the perfume of the honeysuckle. It had been her private sanctuary then, the place where she had dreamed her most secret dreams, and recovered from all the scraped knees and emotional wounds of adolescence.

Amanda glanced out the window again. The fog was lifting, drifting away from the glass and the garden, but it was the magical scent of wild honeysuckle she ached for. Impetuously she reached for the phone.

'I wonder if you could help me,' she said briskly, a few seconds later. 'I'd like to get a flight to LA today, if that's possible. Yes, thank you, I'll hold.'

It took longer than she'd thought. There was no space available until afternoon, there was a car to return and another to rent, but she was in Santa Margarita just after dinnertime. When she pulled up outside the familiar grey-shingled house, there was a tight knot of apprehension in her stomach. Perhaps she should have phoned ahead and let her mother know she was coming. Her mother's old, somewhat battered green Ford was parked in the driveway; a shadowy form moved behind the curtained kitchen window as she sat watching. Gripping her suitcase in her hand, Amanda walked up the narrow path to the house. The old wooden steps to the front porch creaked protestingly, and after a moment's pause she knocked on the door. It opened just a crack, and her mother's sharp voice greeted her.

'Jimmy Franklin, is that you again? I know it's you, Jimmy, fooling around out there, and I'm going to tell your mother, I swear!'

'Mother, it's me. It's Amanda!'

There was the metallic sound of a chain lock being opened, then the door swung back.

'Amanda?' her mother said slowly, staring at her for what seemed an eternity. She wiped her hands on her apron and smoothed back a few strands of greying pale blonde hair that had escaped from her neat chignon. 'Well, for goodness' sakes, Amanda! This is quite a surprise.' She opened the door wide and stepped back. 'Come in, child, come in.'

'How are you, Mother? I suppose I should have called first. . .'

'No, no, of course not.'

The two women stood in the dimly lighted hallway, smiling awkwardly at each other. Amanda put down her suitcase and leaned towards her mother. At the last second, the older woman turned her head to one side and Amanda's hesitant kiss landed on her slightly rouged cheek.

'I'm just so surprised to see you,' she said slowly. 'I heard footsteps, then the knock at the door, and I thought it was young Jimmy Franklin from down the block—do you remember him? He's a good boy, but lately he's taken to ringing the bell, or knocking at the door and then running off. I mean, I assumed it was Jimmy; I couldn't think of anybody else who would. . .' Her voice trailed off lamely and she smiled slightly. 'Just listen to me,' she said briskly, 'running on like this! You must be hungry, Amanda. There's some roast chicken left. I was just putting it away, but I can fix you a plate in no time.'

Amanda followed her mother's thin, straight back into the old-fashioned kitchen. The room looked exactly as she remembered it, and she settled immediately into her old place at the worn pine table.

'I've eaten, thank you, Mother. Some tea would be nice, though,' she added, glancing at the steaming kettle on the stove.

'Are you sure?' her mother asked, reaching into the cabinet for another cup and saucer. 'Last time I was on an airplane, everything tasted like plastic. Of course,' she added quickly, 'it was only a snack. I was just coming back from Sacramento. I guess they serve you a real meal when you fly all the way from New York.'

'I didn't come here from New York,' said Amanda, taking the cup and saucer from her mother's outstretched hand. 'I was in San Francisco, after an assignment, and I just. . .I just suddenly decided it would be nice to come home.'

'What about your office, Amanda? Shouldn't you call your boss? Won't they expect you back?'

'Relax, Mother! I'm on a vacation. Matter of fact, it was my boss who suggested a visit home.'

Her mother sighed and sat down opposite her. 'That's all right then, child. I wouldn't want to think he'd be annoyed with you.' She sipped at her tea and then set the cup down on the saucer. 'How long will you be staying?'

'Well, I have a week or so, Mother. And I have lots to tell you. There's been so much happening to me lately. . .'

'A week?' Her mother frowned slightly and cocked her head to one side. 'Well, we'll try to manage as much time together as we can, Amanda, but I've just expanded the store. Nothing too big, of course; I added a little line of accessories—you know, belts, bags, that sort of thing, and it's brought in some new customers.'

'Actually,' Amanda said, almost shyly, 'I thought. . .I hoped you could take a couple of days off, Mother. We could spend the time here, if you like, or we could drive to some nice little place up in the mountains. I've got a rise, and it would be my treat.'

'A rise! That's wonderful, dear. But I wouldn't let you spend your money so frivolously, even if I could get away. I couldn't possibly leave Mrs Shipper to run the place alone, now could I?'

'I guess not,' Amanda answered. Her mother smiled and sipped her tea. The kitchen was silent except for the ticking of the old clock on the wall above the sink. 'Well, Mother,' she said at last, 'tell me how you've been? You look well.'

'Oh, I'm fine, just fine. I told you, I've expanded the shop and business is picking up. Nothing that would impress a big city, I suppose, but it's pretty good for Santa Margarita.' The older woman rubbed at a tiny spot on the table and cleared her throat. 'Tell me about Morocco. That must have been an important job for you.'

'Oh, it was,' Amanda said eagerly. 'And I did well enough at it, I think. My company promoted me when I got back, just before they sent me to California.'

Her mother smiled broadly and reached over and patted her hand. 'That's wonderful, Amanda. Are you an executive yet? What do they call them—a division head?'

Amanda laughed and shook her head. 'No, not quite. But I did get my own office. It's kind of small, but at least it has my name on the door.'

'Well, you keep up the good work, child, and you'll get there.'

There was another long silence between the two women, and Amanda shifted uneasily on the hard wooden chair. Her mother rose, took the kettle from the stove, and refilled it at the sink.

'More tea, dear? Some cookies, perhaps?'

'Thank you, but I'm fine, really. Anyway, I finished the job I came out to do, and I realised it had been a long time since I came. . .since I was here.' She gave a small, nervous laugh. 'I was sitting in a hotel room in San Francisco, and I got to feeling kind of sorry for myself.'

Her mother's eyes, so like her own except for the tiny lines at their outer edges, widened slightly. 'Why would you feel sorry for yourself, Amanda? Didn't you just tell me you've been promoted? And that you have your own office?'

'Yes, that's true, Mother. It's just that I was alone—I didn't know a soul in the city, and I guess I was feeling a little depressed.' She put down the teaspoon she had been twisting in her fingers and looked up. 'Don't you ever feel like that? Lonely, I mean.'

'Lonely? Why, I haven't the time, child,' the older woman said briskly, pouring freshly boiled water into the teapot. 'I'm at the shop nine hours a day and six on Saturday, and we've begun staying open Friday nights, did I mention that? And then, of course, there's this house,' she added, looking around the spotless kitchen. 'One person doesn't create much of a mess, but it has to be cleaned and scrubbed, just the same.'

'Yes, but—well, when you're not busy, Mother. . .'

Her mother looked at her blankly. 'I'm always busy, Amanda, you must know that. I haven't even taken a day off in—well, I can't remember, but it's been years. Since your high school graduation, probably.'

'You didn't take the whole day then, either,' Amanda said quietly. 'You said it was a Friday, and you could only close the shop half a day, remember?'

Her mother's pale face flushed slightly and her lips narrowed. 'And you made a bit of a fuss, as I recall, Amanda. Seems to me you were old enough to understand that I had an obligation to my customers.'

'But it was a really important day for me, Mother,' Amanda said, amazed at the sudden quiver in her voice. 'There was that luncheon at the school everybody was invited to, and my scholarship honours. . .'

'And I explained to you that I couldn't spare the time,' her mother said sharply. 'Where would we have been if I had worked to turn my shop into something successful, just tell me that? Your father certainly didn't worry about us when he took off, now did he? One cheque— one cheque was all he sent, and after that it was up to me to support us.'

'I know, Mother,' Amanda said quickly, 'and I'm grateful for everything you did, really. But sometimes I think. . .I wonder if there shouldn't be more to life than going to the same job, day after day.'

'What could be more important than making a success of yourself? Answer me that, if you can. I never had to ask a soul for anything, Amanda, and after a while people took notice. I'm on the Chamber of Commerce Executive Board, did you know that?' Her mother's voice had risen sharply and she leaned forward in her chair. 'They know me at the bank, not just here but in the city. The vice-president himself greets me by name, Amanda. When I flew to Sacramento for the day last winter, to apply for a small business loan, you would have been proud of how many recommendations I took with me. Men, business-men, Amanda, see me in the street and know me by name. And people know all about you, child,' she added, more quietly now, a smile on her lips. 'Oh, yes, I boast about you to everyone. You'll go further than I ever dreamed of, Amanda. Truth is, I still have to scrape and bow to my customers. "Yes, Mrs Jones, that dress is most becoming," I say, when I really want to tell the old fool she ought to lose twenty-five pounds. But you, you get to the top, child, and you won't have to say "yes, sir" or "yes, ma'am" to anybody. You won't need a soul, ever. You'll be free in a way I never will be.' Her mother took a deep breath and smiled apologetically. Automatically, her hand went to her hair and smoothed it back. 'It's not like me to make speeches, Amanda, I'm sorry; after all, this is your first night home. But it seems to me we've been through all this before, when you almost ruined everything by marrying that. . .that boy.'

'That was a mistake, Mother. I realised it soon enough, didn't I? Todd was wrong for me.'

'Of course he was wrong for you, Amanda. What could he have given you that you couldn't have provided yourself? As it turned out, you have everything within reach, and you did it all on your own; you're not beholden to anybody for it.'

'You're right, Mother. I guess I thought. . .I wanted someone to be with,' Amanda said hollowly. 'You know, someone to love, to share things with.'

A touch of colour rose to the older woman's cheeks and her nostrils flared distastefully. 'That's the weakness in us that they exploit, Amanda.'

'Are you sure that's what it is?' Amanda asked quickly, her eyes raking over her mother's determined face. 'I mean, I love my job, and I put a lot of time and effort into it. But still sometimes I feel as if I'm missing something. Don't you ever feel that way, Mother? Haven't you ever regretted not having someone?'

Her mother pushed away her cup and saucer and folded her hands on the table in front of her. 'What on earth is wrong with you, child? You walk in here not an hour ago, looking like something the cat dragged in, and now you ask me all these foolish questions! I think you need some rest, Amanda.'

Amanda met her mother's gaze squarely and shook her head. 'They're not foolish to me,' she said quietly.

'Amanda, I thought we settled all this nonsense years ago. You were always such a sensible girl, so bright, so self-sufficient.' The older woman shook her head and sighed deeply. 'I almost wish you hadn't won that scholarship. If you'd gone to the local college here, you'd never have met that. . .that person. He put all these ideas into your head, and you've never got over them, have you?'

'I already said Todd was wrong for me, Mother. He just happened to come along at a time when I needed somebody to care about, to care for.'

'Why are you so weak?' her mother asked fiercely. 'Just because a man whispers a few words into your ear. . .why, there've been men here, right here in this town, Amanda, who tried that nonsense with me. John Atkins—that's right, Mr Atkins who owns the hardware store, kept after me for years, did you know that? But I learned my lesson years ago. I'm not stupid enough to make the same mistake twice.' She snatched up her cup and saucer and walked quickly to the sink, her slippers scuffing softly against the linoleum. 'That's what mistakes are for,' she said, raising her voice over the splashing sound of the water as she neatly rinsed out her dishes. 'You learn from them, grow stronger.' She turned off the water and dried her hands briskly on her apron. 'Did something happen while you were in that place in Morocco?' she demanded suddenly.

'No, not really,' shrugged Amanda, looking down at her teacup.

'Something did,' her mother insisted. 'I can tell. You're not the same, Amanda. I'm not a bit surprised, of course. That climate, that terrible foreign food. . . Were you ill?'

Amanda smiled weakly and shook her head. 'No, nothing like that.' She bent her head and averted her eyes from her mother's piercing stare. 'There was a man,' she said slowly. 'He wanted me to stay with him—well, he wanted me to stay in Morocco. . .it doesn't matter. It's all over, anyway.'

'I knew it,' her mother said bitterly. 'Will you never learn? You've got everything ahead of you, child, everything. Don't regret what you left behind.'

'You're right, Mother,' she answered, more steadily

this time. 'That's why I returned to New York. Did I tell you I've got my name on my office door?' The two women smiled at each other and the tension between them eased. 'I'm sure they'll mention my promotion in the company newsletter. I'll send you the clipping, OK?'

'I'll look forward to it, child. I've started a scrapbook, you know. I'll show it to you tomorrow.' Her mother stretched lightly and looked up at the clock. 'My goodness, look at the time! Why don't you step out into the yard with me, Amanda, while I put out a bowl of milk? There's a stray cat that comes around and I generally leave something out for him.'

'I don't believe it,' teased Amanda, opening the back door and turning on the light that lit the garden. 'You mean you're getting soft in your old age? You, feeding a cat? You wouldn't even let me keep goldfish when I was little.'

'This animal is hardly a pet, Amanda,' her mother said primly, as they walked into the neatly trimmed garden. 'I would have driven him off, but I noticed that there were fewer mice on the place after he turned up. Believe me, he earns his keep.'

They had reached the rear of the garden, a tangle of old rose bushes and overgrown azaleas. Her mother bent to place the bowl on the ground, and Amanda looked around and frowned.

'Where's the old stone wall with the honeysuckle vine that used to be here?'

The older woman straightened up and rubbed the small of her back. 'There's what's left of it,' she said, nodding to an uneven heap of stones. 'I'll have to get one of the neighbourhood boys to haul those rocks out of there one of these days, I suppose.'

'But what happened? It was such a sturdy wall, Mother. And I loved that honeysuckle that grew on it—

the smell of it was wonderful.'

'The smell gave me hayfever,' her mother said flatly. 'Eventually, one day last June, I got tired of sneezing all the time, and I came out here with a trowel and a shovel and I got rid of that awful vine. It went deeper than I thought, way down under the wall and between the stones. Took me the better part of a Sunday; I had a terrible time with it. Then, during the winter, the wall just collapsed. We had lots of rain, you know.'

'It collapsed? Just like that?' Amanda asked incredulously. 'I can't believe it!' An image of another wall and another green vine shimmered like a desert mirage in her mind's eye. 'That wall was so strong.'

'You'd have thought so, wouldn't you? I was surprised, too, but apparently either the wall supported the vine or the vine supported the wall, I don't know which. Anyway, what's the difference?' her mother said briskly, turning back to the house. 'Now the wall is just a pile of stones that needs to be carted away. I think I may dig out these old roses and azaleas, too, then I'll have a nice, clear space back here. Much neater, don't you think?'

'Much neater,' agreed Amanda, following her mother into the kitchen and switching off the garden light.

CHAPTER FOURTEEN

WHEN Amanda awoke the next morning, the old house was empty and silent. Her mother had left for work without awakening her, and Amanda had slept long past the hour at which she usually arose. Barefoot, wrapped in her bathrobe, she padded downstairs to the kitchen and heated the breakfast coffee left in the pot. Sipping at the hot liquid, she wandered into the old pantry her mother used as a small office.

She looked at the walls and smiled; there were clippings stuck neatly on corkboard, starting with an item about her college scholarship clipped from her high school newspaper and ending with the announcement of her posting to Morocco from the Olsen & Tibbs company newsletter. There was a photograph of her mother taken at a Chamber of Commerce dinner and another of an eight-year-old Amanda solemnly holding up a small trophy she had won in a spelling contest.

On the desk was a stiff, formal picture of Amanda and her mother taken the day she had graduated from high school. They were standing shoulder to shoulder, both mother and daughter staring uncomfortably at the camera, Amanda in cap and gown, her mother in one of her 'sensible' dresses. Her mother's arm was around her; that was why the photograph looked so stiff, so wrong, she realised, remembering how the photographer had insisted on the pose. It occurred to her, fleetingly, that there was no other photograph she knew of showing them touching each other. She had passed up her college graduation—she was working at Olsen & Tibbs by then, and couldn't see any sense in taking the day off—but the formal invitation card was in a frame and stood on the desk as well.

The converted pantry backed on to the garden, and Amanda walked to the window and gazed outside to where her mother had left the bowl of milk for the wandering cat. It was, as she expected, gone.

The night before, an hour or so after the two women had said good night and gone to their rooms, Amanda had head the faint creak of the back door. Puzzled, she rose from her bed and went to the window. The moon had risen, and by its pale light she watched as her mother walked to the rear of the garden. A battered yellow tomcat raised his head from the bowl at her approach, and Amanda watched in surprise as her mother bent and stroked his back gently. The cat arched his tail in contentment and rubbed against her legs. Her mother placed another small dish on the ground and the cat buried his face in it and ate. When he had finished, her mother bent again and lifted him into her arms, and the cat settled in snugly against her breast. There was a sense of easy familiarity between the woman and the animal; clearly this was a scene that had been repeated many times over. There was something so poignant, so terribly private and sad about the sight of her mother cradling the tough old tom, that Amanda backed away from the window, leaving them in the silent wash of moonlight, and slipped back into bed with tears stinging her eyes.

She sipped at her coffee and sighed as she looked at the pile of stones that had once been a wall, her own refuge from the world. There was no point in brooding about it, she thought; it was gone, and only painful memory could bring it back. Determined to shake off the gloom she felt, Amanda trotted upstairs and dressed in old jeans and a faded Santa Margarita High School sweatshirt. Downstairs again, she drifted from room to room. The house was as silent as a cemetery; she marvelled at how little of her mother or herself there was to be seen. There were no magazines in the neat living-room, no family photos on the old, out-of-tune piano, no signs of human clutter anywhere except in the tiny pantry office. Everything was spotless, impersonal, and without identity, as if whoever lived here was afraid to leave a mark on anything. In fact, it reminded her of her own three-room apartment in New York City, and it depressed her even further.

'Come on, Sutton,' she said aloud, standing in the middle of the antiseptically clean dining-room. 'What reason have you got to be down, hmm? You're on vacation, remember? You're supposed to be happy, dammit!'

The ringing of the telephone was a welcome intrusion, and she ran back to the kitchen. It was her mother, calling to remind her that there was cold chicken in the refrigerator for lunch.

'Hey, I've got an idea, Mother,' Amanda said impulsively. 'Why don't I change my clothes and pick you up at the shop? I'll take you to the Old Mission Inn for lunch. I bet they still serve great chicken molé! And we'll order wine to celebrate my promotion. How does that sound?'

Her smile faded as her mother patiently explained that she never left the shop during lunch; that was its busiest time. Amanda assured her that she'd be certain to make herself a chicken sandwich and hung up the phone. It had been a mistake to come home, she thought, as a wave of self-pity swept over her. If anything, she felt more alone here, in this house where she had grown up, than she had in San Francisco.

She leafed idly through the morning paper, which looked as untouched as the house itself. There was a

picture on page three of a road graced by a tall stand of
palm trees; the caption beneath explained that they were
endangered by disease, but she thought immediately of
the oasis in the desert, and the unwanted memory of the
hours she had spent there with Nick assailed her so
vividly and unexpectedly that she shivered. Quickly she
turned several pages, and a recipe for couscous and lamb
seemed to leap into bold print. 'This is ridiculous,' she
muttered irritably, slamming the newspaper closed. She
snorted with disbelief. The headline on the back page
screamed: Riverside Grand Prix. Of course, she'd forgotten. The famous track was barely thirty miles away, and
this was the week each year it played host to the world.

Everything was conspiring against her, she thought,
everything was trying to remind her of Nick—and then
she bent over the page of the newspaper, her mouth
suddenly gone dry as the sands of the desert, her pulse
racing as rapidly as the wind across the dunes, as Nick's
name leaped off the page at her. She slapped her hand
down over the list of competing drivers as if she could
make it vanish and took several deep breaths, but when
she dared look again, there it was. Nicholas ben Saad, it
read; it was no mistake, no error, no hallucination. He
was here.

She could be at Riverside in an hour; less than that, if
she didn't stop to change out of her jeans. She could see
him, just get a glimpse of him. 'Why?' a cool, calm voice
inside her asked petulantly, as she moved slowly towards
the stairs. 'Why not?' a different, slightly breathless
voice answered.

'This is foolish,' she told herself as she began to climb
the steps. 'Worse than foolish,' she agreed, as her
footsteps began to hasten. 'This is just plain stupid,' she
warned herself as she snatched her jacket and car keys
from her room, raced back down the stairs and out of the

front door. 'This is the dumbest thing you've ever done,' the cool, calm voice sneered as she put the car into gear and drove quickly towards the highway. But somewhere deep within her, the small, breathless voice was cheering happily.

She hadn't been at Riverside in years, but she moved with easy familiarity once she had arrived. She started to buy a grandstand ticket, but the small voice chastised her and she heard herself ask for a ticket to the pits. They were crowded, as always, with spectators peering over the ropes into the crew areas, and she was positive Nick would never even know she was there, but she pulled a scarf from her pocket and tied it around her head and perched her large, dark sunglasses on her nose. She just wanted to see him one last time, she assured herself, and then she'd leave, go back to her mother's house, go back to New York, to her job, her promotion, her safe, secure life. . .and there he was, his handsome face streaked with grime, his white coveralls spotted with oil, bent over a sleek blue and white Porsche, talking with a man who was busily adjusting something under the car's hood.

Amanda backed away, or at least she wanted to, but people had gathered behind her and she was trapped against the rope, almost close enough to touch him, to reach out to him. Her hands seemed to tremble with the need to grasp his, and she shoved them deep into the back pockets of her jeans before they somehow disgraced her.

'That's Nick ben Saad,' a woman's voice said behind her. 'Isn't he gorgeous?'

'And crazy,' another answered, giggling. 'My boyfriend knows one of the guys in his crew; his team says he's gone nuts. Used to be one of those cold, calculating drivers, you know? The kind that plans out each move. But they say he's done the preliminaries like a madman, taking all kinds of insane chances, even on the ninth turn, you know, the one where they've had all those really bad accidents, the one where those guys got killed? He's been driving like a nut, like he just doesn't give a damn about anything.'

'How well does your boyfriend know him, Bev? I mean, could he, like, introduce me or something?'

The second girl giggled again. 'Are you kidding? Donny knows his mechanic, not him. Anyway, Donny says this guy hasn't even looked at a girl since he got here. I told you, Sally, the guy's gorgeous, but wacky. Forget it.'

Someone's elbow jostled Amanda, someone else stepped on her toes, but still she stood there, unable to take her eyes from Nick. She said nothing, made no sound, although every fibre and nerve within her was crying out his name, until her whole body felt alive with the sound of it. And then, suddenly, Nick's hand shot out and waved the man with him to silence, and he straightened up and ran his hand through his hair. Slowly, his head cocked as if he were listening to something, he began to turn. Amanda stiffened, her heart beginning to race, and pushed her way through the crowd, almost stumbling as she ran towards the stands, but it was too late. He was calling her name, first questioningly, then positively, louder and louder. She could hear his footsteps behind her, then his hands caught her shoulders and spun her around to face him.

'Amanda,' he said softly, a look of wonder on his face, 'Amanda, it's really you.'

She nodded her head, afraid to speak, as he slipped the dark glasses from her nose and gently drew the scarf from her hair.

'I knew it,' he murmured, his hands lingering on her shoulders. She could feel the trembling of her own body, or was it his? 'It was the strangest feeling. . .I was standing there, talking to Don about the car, and suddenly I knew you were here, I just knew it.' His eyes narrowed and his hands dropped to his sides. 'What are you doing here, Amanda? I can't believe you simply had a sudden desire to watch the Grand Prix.'

She shook her head and ran her tongue over her dry lips. 'No, not really. I was at home for a visit—remember, I told you my mother lives near here—and I saw your name in the paper.'

'And?' he prompted, his questioning eyes locked with hers. 'Don't tell me you dropped by to say hello.'

'I don't blame you for not being glad to see me, Nick.' She took a deep breath and plunged her trembling hands deep into her pockets. 'I wasn't going to let you know I was here. I'm sorry if I've intruded.'

'Then why did you come here? If it wasn't to see the race, or talk to me, what was the point?'

A dozen glib, clever answers danced through her thoughts, but in the end she sighed and whispered the only true one. 'I just wanted to see you again.'

Nick put his hands on his hips and studied her. 'Why?' he demanded. 'Why did you want to see me, Amanda?'

She tore her eyes from his and swallowed with difficulty. 'I missed you,' she said, so softly that he had to strain to hear the whispered words. She waited for his answer, while her eyes returned to his face, trying unsuccessfully to read his thoughts, and then finally she began to turn away. 'I'm sorry if I bothered you,' she said. 'I know you must be awfully busy. . .'

He grasped her shoulders and turned her towards him. 'You missed me,' he repeated flatly, his face a mask she couldn't read. 'And what exactly does that mean, Amanda? It's interesting, but a little strange coming from you, isn't it? The last time I saw you, you were too busy with your

career to allow yourself time for me or anything else.
What happened, Amanda? Did you lose your job?'

She winced slightly, but raised her chin. 'I missed
you,' she said, 'and I thought, if I could just see you
again, get a glimpse of you. . .'

'Then what?' he demanded harshly.

'I don't know,' she admitted slowly. 'I didn't plan
any of this, or think that far ahead. I just knew I had to
see you, be near you. . .'

'You've seen me,' he said. 'What next? Do you just go
back home, back to your job. . .'

'You don't understand,' she sighed, tears welling in
her eyes, the words tumbling from her. 'It was being
home that made me understand everything about me,
about the kind of woman I'm becoming. You once told
me to face the truth about myself, Nick,' she said, trying
to steady her voice. 'Well, I have. It may be too late, but
I finally know what it is I really want.'

He looked at her steadily, the grip of his hands biting
into her arms. 'I'm probably a fool to ask,' he said slowly,
'but then I suppose we can't hurt each other any more
than we already have. What is it you really want, Amanda?'

'You,' she said desperately, the word escaping her like
a cry of pain. 'I love you Nick. I never should have left
you—I was afraid to love you—and I've been so empty,
so miserable. . .'

It was as if time had stopped around them. With great
clarity, she saw a muscle twitch in his jaw, saw the set of
his mouth soften, then his arms went around her and the
aching loneliness that had been with her for days, for a
lifetime, was gone, vanishing instantly in the warm magic
of this moment, and nothing was real except the warmth
of his embrace.

'Tell me again, little one,' he demanded. 'I want to
hear you say it.'

'I love you,' she repeated slowly, savouring the sound of the words. 'I think I've known it from the beginning. I love you, and I want to be with you.'

Nick touched her hair gently and she sighed. 'Are you sure?' he asked softly. 'Even if being with me means losing that promotion?'

'The promotion isn't any good without you,' she said simply. 'Nothing is, Nick.'

'If only you knew how I've wanted to hear you say that,' he said, drawing her tightly against him. 'I've been going crazy without you, Amanda. I've been calling your office the last few days, but no one knew where you'd gone. I wanted to find you, shake some sense into you, carry you off, if I had to,' he added, smiling at her. 'Never mind all that. All that matters is that you're here.' He cupped her face in his hands and touched his mouth gently to hers. After a moment he drew back and looked into her shining eyes. 'You have to be certain, Amanda,' he said, almost fiercely. 'In Morocco, you were so afraid of needing me, of losing your independence by admitting it. . .'

She shook her head. 'I won't lose anything,' she said quickly. 'I know that now. Do you remember that wall in the desert? The one at the old fort, with the vine growing out of it? You said the wall and the vine were. . .' She paused when she saw the puzzled expession on Nick's face. 'You see, there was a wall behind my mother's house, and a vine, but my mother pulled it out, and. . .she's so lonely, Nick, did I tell you that? I guess I simply never admitted it to myself before this, but she's so alone. . .' She blinked back her tears and shook her head. 'I'm not making much sense, am I?' she laughed. 'Never mind, I'll explain later. It's kind of complicated.'

'Like you,' he teased, grinning at her.

Amanda smiled and shook her head. 'Not any more,'

she said, then she became aware of the sounds of the crowd in the stands and the sudden squawk of the loudspeaker, and she stirred in Nick's arms. 'Nick, the race. . .it must be starting!'

'I don't give a damn,' he said impatiently. 'Everything I could ever hope to win is right here, in my arms. We have so many plans to make, love, so many things to do. . . Don't ever leave me, Amanda,' he said suddenly.

She drew back slightly and met his gaze. 'Never,' she promised. 'I'll be here as long as you want me. I'm not going anywhere.'

'Yes, you are,' he said quickly. 'You're going to Paris, with me. Tonight, Amanda.' His eyes seemed to search hers. 'Will you do that?'

'Yes, of course,' she whispered. 'And when we get back—well, not then, I hope, but whenever—well, I'm good enough at my work so I can get another job when. . .if I need one. I just want you to know that.'

'Amanda,' Nick said patiently. 'You're not making sense. I can understand that you might want to work, but why would you need to?'

She bit her lip and spoke in an embarrassed whisper. 'You know, Nick. When. . .if I have to.'

He looked as puzzled as if she were speaking in a strange language. 'Amanda, love, I still don't know what you're talking about. I admit, I've been upset since you left, so maybe that explains it. Why would you have to?'

'Please, Nick,' she sighed, 'it's so hard for me to say. But I'll never be a burden to you. If. . .if you change your mind after a while, I can take care of myself. I want to be with you for the rest of my life, but I know. . .I know it may not work out that way.' She lifted her tear-stained face to his and looked at him solemnly. 'I'll be with you for as long as you want me,' she said. 'Do you understand?'

'I want you with me forever, Amanda. I'm not like that fool who let you get away from him.' Nick smiled and brushed her lips with his. 'I want you to marry me, darling. Don't you know that?'

She shook her head, not trusting herself to speak. He stroked her hair and drew her tightly against his chest.

'Forgive me, Amanda,' he murmured. 'I've never proposed before, and I guess I'm not very good at it. I thought you understood what I was asking you that last night we were together. Not only is Paris a perfect place for a honeymoon, but there's a part of my past there that you should know about.' Her smile wavered slightly until she noticed the gleam in his eyes. 'My mother lives in Paris,' he said, kissing the tip of her nose, 'and I always promised her I'd get married in the city where she and my father took their vows. She expected us last week.' He smiled mischievously and hugged her. 'You can have the pleasure of explaining why we never showed up.'

'Oh, Nick,' Amanda sighed, 'I. . .I don't know what to say.'

'Just say "yes",' he laughed, 'unless you want a more traditional proposal; you know, one offered on my knees.' She shook her head, laughing through her tears, and he smiled. 'I wouldn't mind,' he said. 'I'm really kind of old-fashioned at heart.'

Amanda flung her arms around his neck and smiled. 'I love you,' she said, the words rushing out like a triumphant song, 'I love you, I love you. . .'

'And I love you, little one,' he whispered. 'Now and for ever.'

Nick lifted her face to his and kissed her. Above them, the crowds gathered in the stands cheered in wild approval.

Next Month's Romances

Each month you can choose from a world of variety in romance with Mills & Boon. Below are the new titles to look out for next month, why not ask either Mills & Boon Reader Service or your Newsagent to reserve you a copy of the titles you want to buy — just tick the titles you would like to order and either post to Reader Service or take it to any Newsagent and ask them to order your books.

Please save me the following titles:	Please tick	✓
THE WIDOW'S MITE	Emma Goldrick	
A MATTER OF TRUST	Penny Jordan	
A HAPPY MEETING	Betty Neels	
DESTINED TO MEET	Jessica Steele	
THE SEDUCTION STAKES	Lindsay Armstrong	
THE GREEN HEART	Jessica Marchant	
GUILTY PASSION	Jacqueline Baird	
HIDDEN IN THE PAST	Rosemary Gibson	
RUTHLESS LOVER	Sarah Holland	
AN IMPOSSIBLE KIND OF MAN	Kay Gregory	
THE WITCH'S WEDDING	Rosalie Ash	
LOVER'S CHARADE	Rachel Elliot	
SEED OF THE FIRE LILY	Angela Devine	
ROAD TO PARADISE	Shirley Kemp	
FLIGHT OF SWALLOWS	Liza Goodman	
FATHER'S DAY	Debbie Macomber	

If you would like to order these books from Mills & Boon Reader Service please send £1.70 per title to: Mills & Boon Reader Service, P.O. Box 236, Croydon, Surrey, CR9 3RU and quote your Subscriber No:..(If applicable) and complete the name and address details below. Alternatively, these books are available from many local Newsagents including W.H.Smith, J.Menzies, Martins and other paperback stockists from 9th October 1992.

Name:..

Address:..

....Post Code:........................

To Retailer: If you would like to stock M&B books please contact your regular book/magazine wholesaler for details.

You may be mailed with offers from other reputable companies as a result of this application.
If you would rather not take advantage of these opportunities please tick box ☐

WIN A TRIP TO ITALY

Three lucky readers and their partners will spend a romantic weekend in Italy next May. You'll stay in a popular hotel in the centre of Rome, perfectly situated to visit the famous sites by day and enjoy the food and wine of Italy by night. During the weekend we are holding our first International Reader Party, an exciting celebratory event where you can mingle with Mills & Boon fans from all over Europe and meet some of our top authors.

HOW TO ENTER

We'd like to know just how wonderfully romantic your partner is, and how much Mills & Boon means to you.

Firstly, answer the questions below and then fill in our tie-breaker sentence:

1. **Which is Rome's famous ancient ruin?**

   ❏ The Parthenon   ❏ The Colosseum   ❏ The Sphinx

2. **Who is the famous Italian opera singer?**

   ❏ Nana Mouskouri   ❏ Julio Iglesias   ❏ Luciano Pavarotti

3. **Which wine comes from Italy?**

   ❏ Frascati   ❏ Liebfraumilch   ❏ Bordeaux

Tie-Breaker: Well just how romantic is your man? Does he buy you chocolates, send you flowers, take you to romantic candlelit restaurants? Send us a recent snapshot of the two of you (passport size is fine), together with a caption which tells us in no more than 15 words what makes your romantic man so special you'd like to visit Rome with him as the weekend guests of Mills & Boon.

....

....

....

....

In order to find out more about how much Mills & Boon means to you, we'd like you to answer the following questions:

1. **How long have you been reading Mills & Boon books?**

   ❑ One year or less ❑ 2-5 years ❑ 6-10 years

   ❑ 10 years or more

2. **Which series do you usually read?**

   ❑ Mills & Boon Romances ❑ Medical Romances ❑ Best Seller

   ❑ Temptation ❑ Duet ❑ Masquerade

3. **How often do you read them?** ❑ 1 a month or less

   ❑ 2-4 a month ❑ 5-10 a month ❑ More than 10 a month

Please complete the details below and send your entry to: Mills & Boon Reader Service, FREEPOST, P.O. Box 236, Croydon, Surrey CR9 9EL, England.

Name: ....

Address: ....

.... Post Code: ....

Are you a Reader Service subscriber?

❑ No ❑ Yes my Subscriber No. is: ....

_____ RULES & CONDITIONS OF ENTRY _____